SOLID GEOMETRY

HARPER'S MATHEMATICS SERIES

Charles A. Hutchinson, Editor

SOLID
GEOMETRY

A Brief Elementary Course for College Students

J. L. SIMPSON
Montana State College

HARPER & BROTHERS, PUBLISHERS, NEW YORK

SOLID GEOMETRY:
A Brief Elementary Course for College Students
Copyright © 1960 by J. L. Simpson
Printed in the United States of America

Library of Congress catalog card number : 60-7022

Contents

Preface

This text is designed for a brief course in elementary solid geometry for college students, particularly those specializing in engineering and science. The only prerequisites assumed are a knowledge of plane geometry and a little elementary algebra.

The logical development, through the theorems, has been confined mostly to those theorems necessary to obtain measurement formulas. These formulas, together with some from plane geometry, are summarized in Chapters 6 and 7.

A small amount of material on dihedral angles, locus, and the regular polyhedrons has been placed at the end of the text in order that these side issues may not detract from the logical development of the measurement formulas.

Most of the numerical problems have been kept as simple algebraically as possible, consistent with illustrating the solid geometry. Thus it is possible for this course to be taken by students who are concurrently taking a refresher course in algebra as well as by those with better background.

Models made by the students may serve to assist in visualizing some of the theorems. These could be particularly helpful in the first chapter, Lines and Planes in Space, and for Theorems 35, 37, and 42 in addition. In making models planes may be represented by cardboard or thin wood. (A material such as Plexiglass has some advantages.) Lines may be drawn in planes or shown with wire or thread or dowels. Often color may be used to advantage. In the three theorems mentioned, solid models can be very effective.

Some theorems have been outlined only and for some others some reasons have been omitted. Such material can be used for assignments or class discussion. Discussion questions and a few simple original exercises have been included at appropriate points.

This text was designed for a class meeting thirty times with four periods used for examinations. By postulating a few of the more intuitively evident theorems and placing a little less emphasis on proof an even briefer course could be organized.

J. L. S.

SOLID GEOMETRY

CHAPTER I

Lines and Planes in Space

Space, Plane and **Surface** will be taken as undefined terms as well as those taken as such in plane geometry.

The **intersection** of two geometric elements (two planes, two lines, a plane and a line, etc.) is defined to be all the points common to both elements.

Two straight lines in space may have

All points in common—in which case they are said to coincide.

One and only one point in common—in which case they are said to intersect in a point.

No points in common—in which case they are either

both in the same plane—in which case they are said to be *parallel*, or

not both in the same plane—in which case they are said to be *skew*.

The following are characteristics of planes:

Three points, not all in the same straight line (i.e., three noncollinear points) can lie in one and only one plane. (Three noncollinear points determine a plane.)

If two points of a straight line lie in a plane, all points of the straight line lie in the plane.

A straight line and a point not on it can lie in one and only one plane. (A straight line and a point not on it determine a plane.)

Two intersecting straight lines can lie in one and only one plane. (Two intersecting straight lines determine a plane.)

Two parallel lines can lie in only one plane. (Two parallel lines determine a plane.)

Two planes in space may have

All points in common—in which case they are said to coincide.

No points in common—in which case they are said to be parallel.

One straight line, and no other points, in common—in which case the planes are said to intersect in a straight line.

A plane and a straight line in space may have

No points in common—in which case they are said to be parallel.

One and only one point in common—in which case they are said to intersect in a point.

All points of the line lying in the plane. The line is then said to lie in the plane or to be a line of the plane. The plane is said to contain the line.

When reference is made to two lines it will be assumed that two distinct lines are meant, that is, that not *all* the points of one are points of the other. A similar interpretation will be assumed when reference is made to any two elements.

When we speak of a plane *passed through* a line we mean that the plane contains the line. A plane intersecting a line in only one point is *not* considered a plane passed through the line.

Two lines in space will be said to be perpendicular under the same condition that they were perpendicular in plane geometry. This requires that they intersect and therefore that they lie in the same plane (i.e., only coplanar lines can be perpendicular). This definition for perpendicular lines will be used throughout this text. In more advanced mathematics a slightly different definition is often used to include nonintersecting lines as perpendicular under certain conditions.

Perpendicularity of lines and planes and of planes and planes will be defined later.

If more than one possibility exists for any of the conditions, discuss the different cases.

1. How many planes are determined by four points?
2. How many planes are determined by four points taken three at a time?
3. How many planes can be passed through a given straight line?
4. How many planes are determined by two nonintersecting straight lines?
5. How many planes are determined by three concurrent straight lines? (All three straight lines have one and only one point in common.)
6. How many planes are determined by three concurrent straight lines taken two at a time?
7. Is it possible for three planes to have one and only one point in common?
8. Answer question 7 for four planes. Consider also more than four planes.
9. Is a triangle always a plane figure? If so, why? If not, why not?
10. Is a quadrilateral always a plane figure? If so, why? If not, why not?
11. If a straight line lies wholly in a surface, is the surface a plane?

INDIRECT METHOD OF PROOF

Several of the theorems in this chapter use the indirect method of proof (called *reductio ad absurdum*). This is also used in plane geometry. The essential steps are as follow:

1. Assume the contrary of what you are trying to prove.
2. Show by a sequence of logical steps that this leads to a contradiction of a *known fact*. (*Known fact* is here used to mean the given information—a postulate or axiom, or a previously proved theorem.)

3. Reject the hypothesis of the contrary in favor of the statement you are trying to prove.

The method as detailed above will evidently apply only when there are just two possibilities.   Actually it may be extended for a greater number.

NOTE RELATIVE TO DRAWINGS

In the sketches for the following theorems, planes are usually represented by approximately rectangular or triangular portions for convenience, but remember that a plane is actually infinite in extent.

Theorem I. If two straight lines are parallel, every plane containing one and only one of the lines is parallel to the other line.

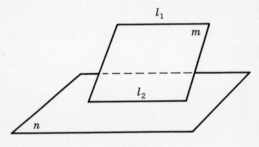

FIG. 1

Given: $l_1 \parallel l_2$

n contains l_2 but not l_1

Assume n is not $\parallel$ to l_1.

This is the first step of the proposed indirect proof.

Then l_1 and n intersect in a point.

This is the only other possibility since it is given that n does not contain l_1.

Let m be the plane determined by l_1 and l_2.

Two parallel lines determine a plane.

Then l_1 intersects l_2 in a point.

Since l_1 lies wholly in m and l_2 consists of all the points in both m and n, this is the only possibility of l_1 intersecting n.

But l_1 does not intersect l_2.

l_1 and l_2 are given as parallel.

∴ reject the assumption that n is not ∥ to l_2 since it leads to this contradiction.

Thus $n \parallel l_1$.

This is the only remaining possibility.

Q.E.D.

Theorem 2. If a line is parallel to a plane, the intersection of that plane with any plane passed through the given line is parallel to the given line.

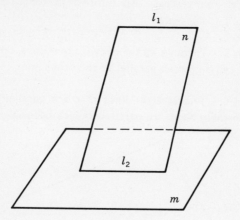

Fig. 2

Given: $l_1 \parallel m$

n contains l_1 and intersects m in l_2

l_1 and l_2 are coplanar.

Assume l_1 intersects l_2.

If so, l_1 intersects m.

But l_1 cannot intersect m.

$\therefore \ l_1 \parallel l_2$.

Q.E.D.

The above is an indirect proof for which reasons should be supplied.

We shall postulate the following three theorems.

Theorem 3.   If each of two intersecting planes is parallel to a given line, the intersection of the planes is parallel to that line.

Theorem 4.   If two intersecting lines are each parallel to a given plane, the plane determined by these lines is parallel to the given plane.

This theorem will be of important use later.   It could well be proved as an exercise.   An indirect proof making use of Theorem 1 is suggested.

Theorem 5.   Through either of two skew lines, one and only one plane can be passed parallel to the other line.

Theorem 6.   Two straight lines that are parallel to a third line not in their plane are parallel to each other.

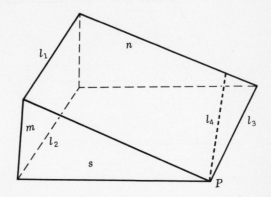

Given:　$l_2 \parallel l_1$
　　　　$l_3 \parallel l_1$

Denote by　m　the plane determined by l_1 and l_2
　　　　　　n　the plane determined by l_1 and l_3
　　　　　　s　the plane determined by l_2 and P, where P is
　　　　　　　　any point on l_3

Then $s \parallel l_1$.　(Why?)

Let l_4 represent the intersection of n and s.　(We intend to show that it coincides with l_3.)

Then $l_4 \parallel l_1$.　(Why?)

But $l_3 \parallel l_1$.　(Given.)

$\therefore$ l_3 and l_4 coincide.　(Why?)

$l_2 \parallel n$.　(Why?)

$l_2 \parallel l_4$.　(Why?)

$l_2 \parallel l_3$.　(Why?)

　　　　　　　　　　　　　　　　　　　　Q.E.D.

Theorem 7. Through a point not in either of two skew lines, one and only one plane can be passed parallel to each of the lines.

l_1 and l_2 are two given skew lines and P a point not in either.

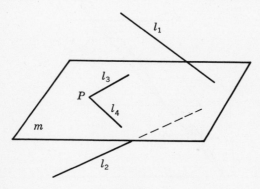

Fɪɢ. 4

Through P draw $l_4 \parallel l_1$ and $l_3 \parallel l_2$. Call m the plane determined
by l_3 and l_4.

Then $m \parallel l_1$ and $m \parallel l_2$. (Why?)

To prove there is only one such plane through P assume there
is another. Call it n (not shown in sketch).

Then the intersection of n and m is parallel to both l_1 and l_2.
(If each of two intersecting planes is parallel to a given line,
their intersection is parallel to the line.)

Then $l_1 \parallel l_2$. (Why?)

But this contradicts the given information.

∴ m is the only such plane.

Q.E.D.

A further restriction should have been placed on the point in
the theorem. What is this restriction?

Theorem 8. The intersections of two parallel planes by a
third plane are parallel lines.

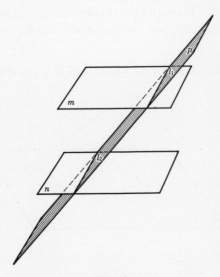

Fig. 5

Given: $m \parallel n$

       p intersects m in l_1

       p intersects n in l_2

l_1 and l_2 are straight lines in p.

Now assume l_1 meets l_2.

To what contradiction does this lead?

From this contradiction we then reject the assumption and accept the theorem as the only other possibility. (How did we reject the idea that the intersections might be skew lines?)

QUESTIONS

1. Is it possible for three planes to intersect so as to have only one point common to all three planes?
2. Is it possible for four or more planes to intersect so as to have only one point common to all the planes?
3. What is the smallest number of lines of intersection that can be formed by three distinct planes?
4. What is the greatest number of lines of intersection that can be formed by three distinct planes?
5. Given two skew lines is it possible to pass a plane through one of them and parallel to the other?
6. Given two parallel lines are all planes passed through one of them parallel to the other?
7. Given two parallel planes are all lines drawn in one of the planes parallel to the other plane?
8. Given two parallel planes are all lines drawn in one parallel to a given line in the other?

Definitions

A line is said to be **perpendicular to a plane** if it is perpendicular to every line in the plane passing through its point of intersection with the plane. (This point is called the foot of the perpendicular.) The plane is said to be perpendicular to the line.

Lines other than perpendiculars intersecting a plane in a point are said to be **oblique to the plane.**

The **distance from a point to a plane** is the length of the perpendicular from the point of the plane.

The definition for a line perpendicular to a plane would be inconvenient or impossible to use to determine whether or not a certain line was perpendicular to a certain plane. However, Theorem 9 shows that if a certain relatively simple condition is satisfied the requirement of the definition is also met.

The following theorem could have been given as the definition and then the definition would have followed as a theorem. (The proof would have been very similar.)

Theorem 9. If a line is perpendicular to each of two intersecting lines at their point of intersection, it is perpendicular to the plane of the two lines.

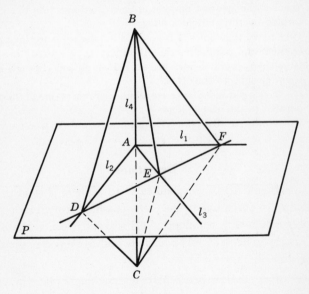

Fig. 6

Given: $l_4 \perp l_1$ at A and $l_4 \perp l_2$ at A

Let l_3 be any other line through A in the plane (P) of l_1 and l_2.

Lay off $AB = AC$ on l_4.

Draw DF in P intersecting l_2 in D, l_3 in E, and l_1 in F.

Draw CD, CE, CF, BD, BE, and BF.

$BD = DC$ and $BF = CF$.   (Why?)

$DF = DF$.   (Identity.)

$\triangle BDF \cong \triangle CDF$.   (Why?)

Now show $\triangle BDE \cong \triangle CDE$.

Then $BE = EC$.   (Why?)

$AE = AE$.   (Identity.)

$\triangle BAE \cong \triangle CAE$.   (Why?)

$\therefore \angle BAE = \angle CAE$.   (Why?)

$l_4 \perp l_3$.   (Why?)

$l_4 \perp P$.   (Why?)

Q.E.D.

Theorem 10. All the perpendiculars to a given line at a given point lie in a plane which is perpendicular to the given line at that point.

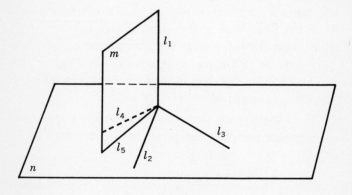

Fig. 7

Given: l_2 and l_3, two perpendiculars to l_1 at P

Denote by n the plane determined by l_2 and l_3.

Let l_4 represent any other perpendicular to l_1 at P.

Denote by m the plane determined by l_1 and l_4.

Denote by l_5 the line of intersection of m with n.

Assume l_4 does not coincide with l_5 (i.e., that it does not lie in n).

But $l_1 \perp l_5$. (Since $l_1 \perp n$ at P it is perpendicular to every line in n through P).

But $l_1 \perp l_4$. (Given.)

Then l_4 and l_5 are two perpendiculars to l_1 at P and lie in the same plane. This is impossible (from plane geometry).

$\therefore$ l_4 and l_5 coincide and so all the $\perp$s to l_1 at P lie in n.

Q.E.D.

The following theorem may now be easily proved:

Theorem II. Oblique lines drawn from any point in a perpendicular to a plane that meet the plane at equal distances from the foot of the perpendicular are equal, and conversely.

The following exercises are similar to the above theorem:

1. Prove that equal obliques drawn from a point in a perpendicular to a plane make equal angles with the lines joining their feet to the foot of the perpendicular.

2. Prove that if two obliques are drawn from a point in a perpendicular to a plane so as to make equal angles with the lines joining their feet to the foot of the perpendicular, the obliques are equal.

Of the above three proofs (one theorem and two exercises) the student should complete the proof, with a drawing, for at least one.

The following two theorems are relatively straightforward extensions of plane geometry and will be taken as postulates

Theorem 12.   Of two oblique lines that are drawn from a point in a perpendicular to a plane and meet the plane at unequal distances from the foot of the perpendicular, the more remote is the greater, and conversely.

Theorem 13.   From a given external point the perpendicular to a plane is shorter than any oblique from that point.

In the following four theorems note that for each theorem there are two things to be proved: (1) that there is a line or plane satisfying the given condition; (2) that this is the only such line or plane.

Theorem 14.   Through a given point in a given line, one and only one plane can be passed perpendicular to the line.

Theorem 15.   Through a given point outside a given line, one and only one plane can be passed perpendicular to the line.

Theorem 16.   Through a given point in a given plane, one and only one line can be drawn perpendicular to the given plane.

Theorem 17.   Through a given point outside a given plane, one and only one line can be drawn perpendicular to the given plane.

Our development of solid geometry to this point would enable us to prove all four of these theorems.   For a short course, however, we shall postulate the first three and prove only the last one.

Theorem 17.   Through a given point outside a given plane, one and only one line can be drawn perpendicular to the given plane.

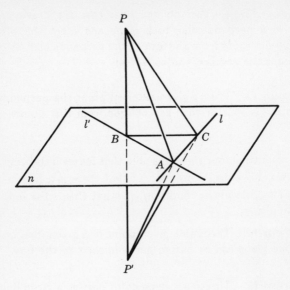

FIG. 8

Given: Point P external to plane n

Required: A line from P perpendicular to n.

Let l be any line in n.

Pass a plane through P, perpendicular to l, and intersecting l in A and n in l'.

Draw $PB \perp l'$.

Now we prove that PB is the required perpendicular to n.

   Let C be any point other than A in l and draw BC.

   Extend PB to P' making $PB = BP'$ and drawn $P'A$ and $P'C$.

   Now show $\triangle P'AC \cong \triangle PAC$ to get $PC = P'C$.

   Then show $\triangle PBC \cong \triangle P'BC$ to get $\angle PBC = \angle P'BC$.

   Then $PB \perp n$.

(Details of the proof should be supplied by the student.)

To prove uniqueness

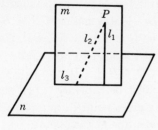

Fig. 9

Assume there exists another perpendicular (call the first one
l_1 and the second l_2).

Then l_1 and l_2 determine a plane m.

Call the intersection of m and n l_3.

Then in m, l_1 and l_2 are both perpendicular to l_3 from P, and
this is impossible (from plane geometry).

∴ the perpendicular is unique.

Q.E.D.

Theorem 18.   Two lines perpendicular to the same plane are
parallel.

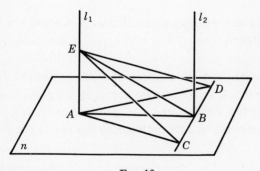

Fig. 10

Given: $l_1 \perp n$ and $l_2 \perp n$

Draw AB connecting feet of the perpendiculars.

Through B draw $DC \perp AB$ making $CB = BD$.

Choose a point E on l_1 and draw EC, ED, EB, AC, and AD.

Use some congruent triangles to prove $EB \perp CD$.

Now since $EB \perp CD$, $AB \perp CD$, and $l_2 \perp CD$,

  EB, AB, and l_2 must be coplanar. (All the perpendiculars
  to a given line at a given point lie in a plane which is perpendicular to the given line at that point.)

EA lies in this same plane. (Why?)

Since l_1 and l_2 are coplanar and both perpendicular to AB
  they are parallel (from plane geometry).

Q.E.D.

The following three theorems may now be proved. If not
  proved they should be postulated for possible future reference.

Theorem 19. If one of two parallel lines is perpendicular to
a plane, the other is also perpendicular to the plane. (If a plane
is perpendicular to one of two parallel lines, it is perpendicular
to the other also.)

Theorem 20. All lines perpendicular to a plane are parallel
to each other.

Theorem 21. If from the foot of a perpendicular to a plane
a straight line is drawn at right angles to any given line in the
plane, the line connecting their intersection to any point in
the perpendicular is perpendicular to the line in the plane.

Theorem 22. Two planes perpendicular to the same line are
parallel.

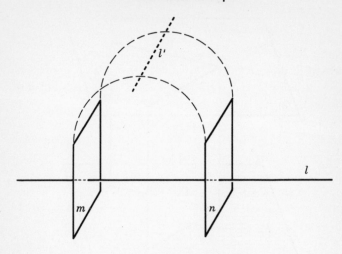

Fig. 11

Given: $m \perp l$ and $n \perp l$

Assume m is not parallel to n.

Then they intersect in a line—call it l'.

Let P be any point in l'.

Then m and n cannot both be perpendicular to l.
 (Why not?)

This contradicts the given information.

$\therefore$ $m \parallel n$ (only remaining possibility).

Q.E.D.

Theorem 23.   If a straight line is perpendicular to one of two parallel planes, it is perpendicular to the other.

Given: $m \parallel n$
            $l_1 \perp n$

Pass two planes through l_1 intersecting m in l_4 and l_5 and
  intersecting n in l_2 and l_3.

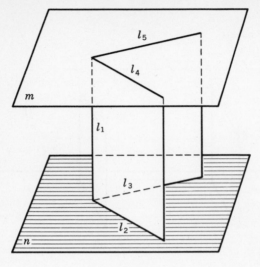

FIG. 12

$l_4 \parallel l_2$ and $l_5 \parallel l_3$ (Why?)

$l_1 \perp l_3$ and $l_1 \perp l_2$.   (Why?)

$\therefore$ $l_1 \perp l_4$ and $l_1 \perp l_5$.   (Why?)

$\therefore$ $l_1 \perp m$.   (Why?)

Q.E.D.

We could now prove but will postulate instead, in the interest of brevity:

Theorem 24.   Through a given point outside a given plane, one and only one plane can be passed parallel to the given plane.

Theorem 25.   If two straight lines are cut by three parallel planes, their corresponding segments are proportional.

Given: Lines AB and CD cut by the parallel planes m, n, and p

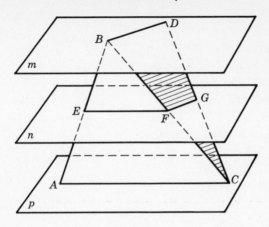

Fig. 13

$EF \parallel AC$ and $FG \parallel BD$.   (Why?)

$\dfrac{BE}{EA} = \dfrac{BF}{FC}$ and $\dfrac{DG}{GC} = \dfrac{BF}{FC}$.   (From plane geometry.)

$\therefore \dfrac{BE}{EA} = \dfrac{DG}{GC}$ (Why?)

Theorem 26. If two angles not in the same plane have their sides respectively parallel and extending from their vertices in the same direction, they are equal and their planes are parallel.

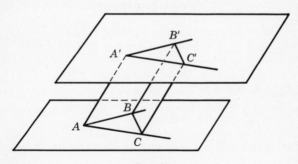

Fig. 14

Given: $AB \parallel A'B'$ and $AC \parallel A'C'$

Take $AB = A'B'$ and $AC = A'C'$.

$AA'C'C$ and $AA'B'B$ are parallelograms.

$BB' \parallel AA'$ and $BB' = AA'$

$CC' \parallel AA'$ and $CC' = AA'$

$BB' \parallel CC'$ and $BB' = CC'$

$BB'C'C$ is a parallelogram.

$B'C' = BC$.

$\triangle A'B'C' \cong \triangle ABC$.

$\angle C'A'B' = \angle CAB$.

Q.E.D. (first part)

$A'B'$ and $A'C'$ are parallel to the plane of AB and AC. (If two straight lines are parallel, every plane containing one and only one of the lines is parallel to the other line.)

The planes of the angles are parallel. (If two intersecting lines are each parallel to a given plane, the plane determined by these lines is parallel to the given plane.)

Q.E.D. (second part)

Reasons for the first nine statements following Theorem 26 should be supplied.

PROBLEMS

For the following problems the lettering refers to Fig. 13, used with Theorem 25.

1. If $AE = 6$, $EB = 8$, $DG = 15$, find CG.
2. If $AE = 8$, $EB = 6$, $CG = 24$, find DG.
3. If $AB = 48$, $DG = 18$, $CG = 24$, find AE and EB.
4. If $DC = 20$, $AE = 5$, $EB = 10$, find DG and GC.
5. If AE is three times as long as EB and $DG = 6$, find GC.
6. If AE is four times as long as EB and $DC = 27$, find DG and GC.

QUESTIONS

1. Through a given point outside a given plane, how many lines may be passed parallel to the given plane?
2. Through a given point outside a given plane, how many planes may be passed parallel to the given plane?
3. Through a given point on a given line, how many planes may be passed perpendicular to the given line?
4. Through a given point in a given line, how many lines may be passed perpendicular to the given line?

CHAPTER 2

Polyhedrons

We shall take **geometric solid** as an undefined term.

A **polyhedron** is a geometric solid bounded by plane polygons.

The **faces** of the polyhedron are the plane polygons bounding
the polyhedron.

The **edges** of a polyhedron are the intersections of the faces.

The **vertices** of a polyhedron are the intersections of the
edges.

A **diagonal** of a polyhedron is a straight-line segment joining
two vertices not in the same face. A straight-line segment
joining two nonadjacent vertices in the same face is called
a **face diagonal**.

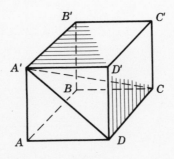

Fig. 15

EXAMPLE (see polyhedron, Fig. 15)

The six faces are rectangles: examples are $ABCD$ and $D'C'CD$.

The vertices are the points A, B, C, D, A', B', C', D'.

There are twelve edges: examples are $A'B'$, AD, DD'.

A diagonal is $A'C$.   There are three others that are not shown.
A face diagonal is $A'D$.   There are eleven others that are not
shown.

Regular polyhedrons are polyhedrons all of whose faces are
congruent regular polygons.

Convex polyhedrons are polyhedrons such that no face, if
produced, will enter the polyhedron.

Two examples of regular polyhedrons:

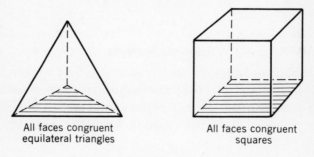

All faces congruent
equilateral triangles

All faces congruent
squares

Fig. 16

Two examples of polyhedrons that are not regular:

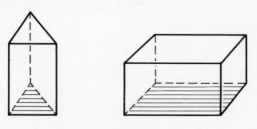

Fig. 17

The four polyhedrons illustrated in Figs. 16 and 17 are all
convex polyhedrons.   An example of a polyhedron that is

not convex is shown in Fig. 18.   Such polyhedrons are called
concave polyhedrons.

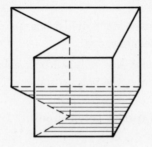

Fig. 18

Prismatic Surfaces

A prismatic surface is the surface generated by a straight line
(*e*) which moves so as to continuously intersect the boundary
of a given polygon (*P*) and remains always parallel to a given
line (*l*) where (*l*) is not coplanar with (*P*).   See Fig. 19.

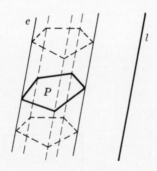

Fig. 19

Note that a prismatic surface is of infinite extent.

The following terminology will be adopted for prismatic
surfaces:

An **element** of the prismatic surface is the line (*e*) in any of its positions.

An **edge** of the prismatic surface is an element through a vertex of the polygon (*P*).

A **face** of the prismatic surface is the portion of the prismatic surface contained between two consecutive edges. Note that a face of a prismatic surface is of infinite extent.

Prisms

A **prism** is a polyhedron bounded by a prismatic surface and two parallel planes.

A **base** of a prism is a polygon bounded by the intersection of the prismatic surface and one of the two parallel planes.

A **lateral face** of a prism is the portion of a face of the prismatic surface included between the two bases.

A **lateral edge** of a prism is the portion of an edge of the prismatic surface included between the bases.

The **lateral area** of a prism is the sum of the areas of the lateral faces.

The **total area** of a prism is the sum of the lateral area and the areas of the bases.

The **altitude** of a prism is the length of any perpendicular from one base to the plane of the other base.

A **right prism** is a prism whose lateral edges are perpendicular to the planes of its bases.

An **oblique prism** is a prism whose lateral edges are not perpendicular to the planes of its bases.

A **regular prism** is a right prism whose bases are regular polygons.

Prisms are classified as triangular, quadrangular, pentagonal, etc., according to the shapes of their bases.

A **right section** of a prism is the polygon formed by a plane intersecting all the lateral faces (or the lateral faces extended) so as to cut all the lateral edges at right angles.

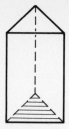 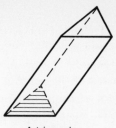

A triangular
right prism

A triangular
oblique prism

FIG. 20

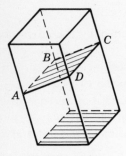 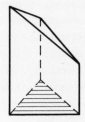

An oblique prism
with a square base
ABCD is a right section

A truncated prism
Note that this is not a prism

FIG. 21

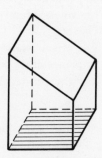

Another
truncated prism

FIG. 22

A truncated prism is that part of a prism included between a base and a plane, not parallel to the base, cutting all the lateral edges.

The following theorems relating to prisms may now be easily proved:

Theorem 27. The lateral faces of a prism are parallelograms.

(Show that the opposite sides are parallel.)

Theorem 28. The lateral edges of a prism are equal.

(This and Theorem 29 follow almost immediately from Theorem 27.)

Theorem 29. The lateral faces of a right prism are rectangles.

Theorem 30. The lateral area of a prism is equal to the product of the length of a lateral edge and the perimeter of a right section.

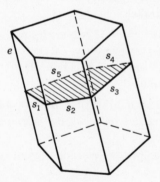

Fig. 23

For the pentagonal prism shown in Fig. 23 let e represent the length of a lateral edge and consider a right section, the lengths of whose sides are s_1, s_2, s_3, s_4, and s_5.

The lateral area is then the sum of the areas of the lateral faces:

$$A = es_1 + es_2 + es_3 + es_4 + es_5$$

Or

$$A = e(s_1 + s_2 + s_3 + s_4 + s_5)$$

Or, since $s_1 + s_2 + s_3 + s_4 + s_5 = p$ (the perimeter of a right section)

$$A = ep.$$

Although illustrated for a pentagonal prism, it should be evident that this formula will be applicable to a prism of any number of sides.

Note that in the case of a *right* prism the lateral area is still given by the same formula, only in this case the perimeter of a right section is the perimeter of the base and the length of a lateral edge is the altitude of the prism.

A **parallelepiped** is a prism whose bases are parallelograms.

Theorem 31. The opposite faces of a parallelepiped are congruent and parallel.

(To prove parallel use: "If two angles not in the same plane have their sides respectively parallel and extending from their vertices in the same direction, they are equal and their planes are parallel.")

From the above it follows that *if three adjacent faces of a parallelepiped are rectangles, all the faces are rectangles.*

A **right parallelepiped** is a right prism whose bases are parallelograms.

A **rectangular parallelepiped** is a parallelepiped all of whose faces are rectangles.

A **cube** is a rectangular parallelepiped in which three edges meeting a common point are equal. (Therefore it follows that the faces of a cube are squares.)

Summary of Classification of Polyhedrons

polyhedrons
  prisms
    parallelepipeds
      right parallelepiped
        rectangular parallelepipeds
          cubes

The **volume** of a geometric solid is a quantitative measure of the amount of space inclosed by the solid. (**Space** is taken as an undefined term.)

The **volume of a rectangular parallelepiped** is the product of the numerical measures, expressed in the same units, of the lengths of any three edges having a common vertex. To this product the label *cubic units* (whatever the units used for measuring the edges were) will be attached.

The statement above is equivalent to the usual formula:

$$V = LWH$$

Where L, W, and H represent the three dimensions, usually called length, width, and height.

We will have reason to cite the formula in the form:

$$V = Bh$$

Where B is the area of the base and h the corresponding altitude to that base.

We shall use *equal solids* to mean *equal in volume* and *not necessarily* congruent solids. Congruent solids will be assumed to have equal volumes.

The following theorems are here postulated and will be used in obtaining some more volume formulas:

Theorem 32. Two right prisms are congruent if they have equal altitudes and congruent bases.

Theorem 33. Two truncated right prisms are congruent if their bases are congruent and their corresponding edges are respectively equal and similarly placed.

(Proofs of these theorems could be done by superposition.)

QUESTIONS BASED ON THE DEFINITIONS FOR POLYHEDRONS

1. Are all rectangular parallelepipeds prisms?
2. Are all polyhedrons prisms?
3. Are all prisms parallelepipeds?
4. Are all right prisms parallelepipeds?
5. Are all prisms polyhedrons?
6. Are all rectangular parallelepipeds cubes?
7. Are all cubes rectangular parallelepipeds?
8. Does there exist a right prism that is a parallelepiped?
9. Does there exist a truncated prism that is a parallelepiped?
10. Does there exist an oblique prism that is a parallelepiped?
11. Does there exist a triangular prism that is a parallelepiped?

For each of the above the student should be able to supply a reason for his answer.

PROBLEMS

1. For a rectangular parallelepiped 4″ × 6″ × 8″ find the total area.
2. For the parallelepiped in Problem 1 find the length of each face diagonal.
3. Find the length of a diagonal (sometimes called a *main* or *principal* diagonal) of the parallelepiped in Problem 1.
4. Find the volume of the parallelepiped in Problem 1.
5. Find the lateral area of a hexagonal right prism if a side of the base is 3 inches and the altitude of the prism is 8 inches.
6. Find the lateral area of a triangular right prism whose base is a right triangle with legs 6 inches and 8 inches if the altitude of the prism is 12 inches.
7. Find the edge of a cube whose volume is 125 cubic inches.
8. Find the length of a face diagonal of the cube in Problem 7.
9. Find the length of a diagonal of the cube in Problem 7.

10. Find the lateral area of a triangular prism whose right section is a triangle whose sides are 6 inches, 8 inches, and 12 inches if a lateral edge of the prism is 5 inches.
11. Find the edge of a cube whose volume is to be twice that of a cube whose edge is 3 inches.
12. If the edge of a cube is doubled, what change takes place in the volume.
13. If the edge of a cube is doubled, what change takes place in the total area?

Theorem 34. Sections of a prism made by parallel planes which cut all the lateral edges are congruent polygons.

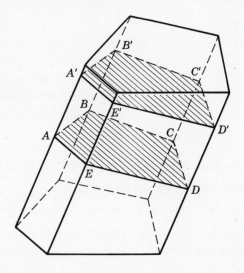

Fig. 24

Let the prism shown be cut by two parallel planes resulting in the sections $ABCDE$ and $A'B'C'D'E'$.

1. $AB \parallel A'B'$ $BC \parallel B'C'$ and so on.	1. If two parallel planes are cut by a third plane the lines of intersection are parallel.

2. $\angle ABC = \angle A'B'C'$
   $\angle BCD = \angle B'C'D'$
   and so on.

2. If two angles have their arms respectively parallel and extending in the same direction from the vertex, the angles are equal.

3. The portions of the faces of the prism included between the sections are parallelograms.

3. Why?

4. $AB = A'B'$
   $BC = B'C'$
   and so on.

4. Opposite sides of a parallelogram are equal.

5. The polygons $ABCDE$ and $A'B'C'D'E'$ are congruent.

5. If the angles and sides of one polygon are equal respectively to the angles and sides of another polygon, the polygons are congruent.

Q.E.D.

Slight extensions of Theorem 34 give the following:

The bases of a prism are congruent polygons.

All right sections of a prism are congruent polygons.

A section of a prism made by a plane parallel to the base is congruent to the base.

Theorem 35. An oblique prism is equal to a right prism whose base is a right section of the oblique prism and whose altitude is equal to a lateral edge of the oblique prism.

Given: The oblique prism with bases $ABCDE$ and $A'B'C'D'$ E' (denoted hereafter as $A'—ABCDE$)

$FGHIK$ is a right section.

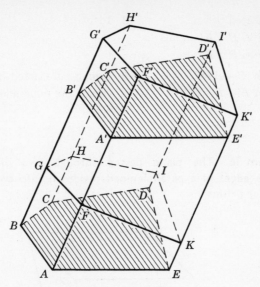

Fig. 25

Extend the edges of the prism.

$F'G'H'I'K'$ is a section by a plane parallel to $FGHIK$, at a
distance $FF' = AA'$.

1. $AA' = BB' = CC'$, etc.   1. Lateral edges of a prism are
   $FF' = GG' = HH'$, etc.   equal.

2. $AF = A'F'$ 2. Why?
   $BG = B'G'$
   and so on.

3. $FGHIK \cong F'G'H'I'K'$.   3. Bases of a prism are
                                    congruent.

4. The truncated right prisms   4. The applicable theorem was
   B—$FGHIK$ and   postulated.
   B'—$F'G'H'I'K'$ are con-
   gruent and therefore equal.

5. Truncated prism
   $B—F'G'H'I'K'$ equals
   $B—F'G'H'I'K'$.

5. Identity.

6. Prism $A'—ABCDE =$
   prism $F'—FGHIK$.

6. Equals subtracted from
   equals the remainders are
   equal.

Q.E.D.

Theorem 36. The plane passed through two diagonally opposite edges of a parallelepiped divides it into two equal triangular prisms.

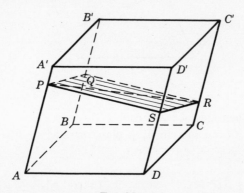

Fig. 26

Given: The parallelepiped with bases $ABCD$ and $A'B'C'D'$

Consider the plane passed through AA' and CC'.
Consider also the right section $PQRS$.

1. $PQRS$ is a parallelogram.
2. Triangle PQR is congruent to triangle PSR.
3. $\triangle PQR$ and $\triangle PSR$ are right sections (by definition) of the triangular prisms whose bases are ABC and ADC respectively.
4. The triangular prism whose base is ABC is equal to a right

prism with base PQR and altitude equal to AA'. The triangular prism whose base is ADC is equal to a right prism whose base is PSR and altitude equal to AA'. (Note that these right prisms do not appear in the drawing.)
5. The two right prisms mentioned above are equal.
6. Therefore the two triangular prisms with bases ABC and ADC are equal.

Q.E.D.

Only the statements for the proof are supplied above—reasons should be supplied.

Theorem 37. The volume of any parallelepiped is equal to the product of the area of its base and its altitude.

(To insure generality we shall assume the "worst" case; i.e., that the given parallelepiped "leans both ways".)

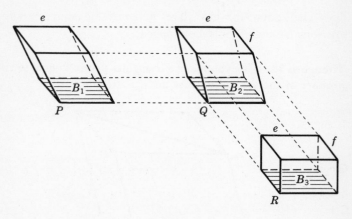

Fig. 27

Given: The parallelepiped P

Extend the edge e and all edges parallel to it.

Pass two parallel planes perpendicular to these edges extended and a distance apart equal to e, forming the parallelepiped Q. (How do we know Q is a parallelepiped?)

Extend the edge f of Q and all edges parallel to it.

Pass two parallel planes perpendicular to these edges extended
and a distance apart equal to f, forming the rectangular
parallelepiped R. (How do we know R is a rectangular
parallelepiped?)

1. $P = Q$ and $Q = R$.
2. $P = R$.
3. P, Q, and R have the same altitude. (We shall denote this
   common altitude by h.)
4. $B_1 = B_2$ and $B_2 = B_3$ (equal in area).
5. $B_1 = B_3$.
6. Volume of $R = B_3 h$.
7. Volume of $P = B_1 h$.

Q.E.D.

Only the statements have been given in the above proof—
reasons for each should be supplied.

Theorem 38. The volume of a triangular prism is equal to the
product of the area of its base and its altitude.

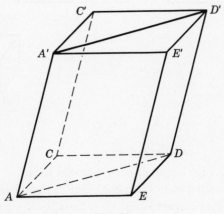

FIG. 28

Given: The triangular prism whose bases are AED and $A'E'D'$

Pass plane $AA'C'C$ through AA' and parallel to plane $EE'D'D$.
Pass plane $CC'D'D$ through DD' and parallel to plane $AA'E'E$.
Denote the base AED of the triangular prism by B.
Denote the common altitude of the triangular prism and the parallelepiped whose bases are $ACDE$ and $A'C'D'E'$ by h.

1. The volume of the given triangular prism is one-half the volume of the parallelepiped. (Why?)
2. The base of the parallelepiped is $2B$. (Why?)
3. The volume of the parallelepiped is $2Bh$. (Why?)
4. The volume of the triangular prism is therefore equal to Bh. (Why?)

Q.E.D.

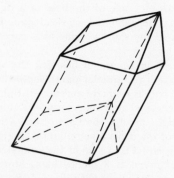

Fig. 29

Since any prism may be divided into triangular prisms we have as a result that the volume of *any* prism is equal to the product of its base and its altitude. (The formal statement of the steps of this proof will not be given here.)

For any prism of base B and altitude h: $V = Bh$.

PROBLEMS

1. Find the volume of an octagonal right prism if the area of its base is 80 square inches and the altitude of the prism is 7 inches.

2. Find the volume of a hexagonal right prism if the side of the base is 4 inches and the altitude of the prism is 5 inches.

3. Find the volume of a triangular right prism if the base is a triangle with legs 6 inches and 8 inches and altitude of the prism is 12 inches.

4. Find the volume of a triangular right prism whose base is a triangle whose sides are 6 inches, 8 inches, and 12 inches, if the altitude of the prism is 5 inches.

5. A certain rectangular parallelepiped has a volume of 200 cubic inches. If the base is a square and the altitude of the parallelepiped is 8 inches, find the length of a side of the base.

6. Find the volume of a triangular right prism if the base is an equilateral triangle 2 inches on a side and the height of the prism is 4 inches.

7. If the diagonal of a cube is 9 inches, what is the volume of the cube?

8. Find the length of a side of the base of a right prism whose base is a regular hexagon and whose altitude is 4 inches if the prism is to have the same volume as a cube 4 inches on an edge.

9. The lateral area in square inches and the volume in cubic inches of a certain rectangular parallelepiped are numerically equal. If the base is a square and the altitude of the parallelepiped is 6 inches, what is the length of a side of the base?

10. Given: Two right prisms, the base of one a regular hexagon and the base of the other an equilateral triangle. If a side of the hexagon is equal to a side of the equilateral triangle and the hexagonal prism is 8 inches high, how high must the triangular prism be to have the same volume as the hexagonal prism?

Pyramids

A **pyramid** is a polyhedron, one of whose faces is a polygon of any number of sides, and whose other faces are triangles having a common vertex.

The **base** of the pyramid is the nontriangular face of the polyhedron. (If all faces are triangular, one face is arbitrarily selected as the base.)

The **vertex** of a pyramid is the common vertex of the triangular faces of the polyhedron.

The **lateral faces** of a pyramid are those faces other than the base.

The **lateral area** of a pyramid is the sum of the areas of the lateral faces.

The **total area** of a pyramid is the sum of the lateral area and the area of the base.

The **altitude** of a pyramid is the perpendicular from the vertex to the plane of the base.

A **regular pyramid** is a pyramid whose base is a regular polygon and whose altitude intersects the center of the base. (Note that it is not sufficient for the base to be a regular polygon—there are two conditions to be satisfied for regular pyramids.)

The **slant height** of a pyramid is the altitude of one of the lateral faces. (Note that this is not unique and therefore not defined *except* for regular pyramids.)

The **lateral edges** of a pyramid are the sides of the faces not common to the base.

It can easily be shown that:

All the lateral edges of a regular pyramid are equal.

All the lateral faces of a regular pyramid are congruent isosceles triangles.

Theorem 39. The lateral area of a regular pyramid is equal to half the product of its slant height and the perimeter of its base.

If we denote the slant height by s and a side of the base by b, the area of one lateral face will be $\frac{1}{2} sb$. If there are n

lateral faces the lateral area will be $\frac{1}{2}snb$, or since nb is the perimeter of the base (p), the lateral area (A) will be given by $A = \frac{1}{2}ps$.

NOTE FOR SOLVING PROBLEMS

If the altitude and the side of the base are given, the slant height may be determined by applying the Pythagorean theorem.

EXAMPLE I

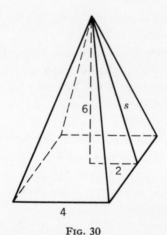

6   s

2

4

FIG. 30

Given: A regular square pyramid with altitude 6 inches, side of the base 4 inches.   To find the lateral area:

$$s^2 = 2^2 + 6^2 \qquad A = \frac{1}{2}(16)(2\sqrt{10})$$

$$s^2 = 40 \qquad\qquad A = 16\sqrt{10} \text{ sq. in.}$$

$$s = \sqrt{40}$$

$$s = 2\sqrt{10}$$

Example II

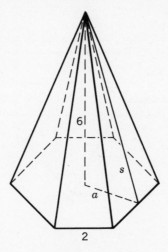

Fig. 31

Given: A regular hexagonal pyramid with altitude 6 inches, side of the base 2 inches.   To find the lateral area:

$$a = \frac{b\sqrt{3}}{2} \qquad\qquad A = \frac{1}{2}(12)\sqrt{39}$$

$$a = \frac{2\sqrt{3}}{2} = \sqrt{3} \qquad A = 6\sqrt{39} \text{ sq. in.}$$

$$s^2 = 6^2 + (\sqrt{3})^2$$

$$s = \sqrt{39}$$

Theorem 40. If a pyramid is cut by a plane parallel to the base, the lateral edges and the altitude are divided proportionally, and the section is a polygon similar to the base.

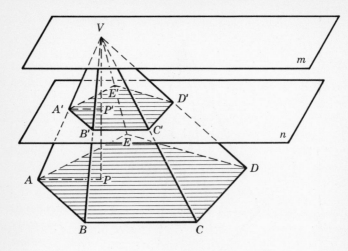

FIG. 32

Given: The pyramid V—$ABCDE$ cut by n parallel to the base forming section $A'B'C'D'E'$

Pass plane m through V parallel to n.

From V drop a perpendicular to the base intersecting the base in P and the section in P'.

Draw $A'P'$.

VA and VP determine a plane.

$A'P' \parallel AP$.

Now show some triangles similar to get $\dfrac{VA'}{VA} = \dfrac{VP'}{VP}$.

Q.E.D. (first part)

Now show $\triangle VA'B' \sim \triangle VAB$ and $\triangle VB'C' \sim \triangle VBC$, etc., to get

$$\frac{VA'}{VA} = \frac{A'B'}{AB} = \frac{VB'}{VB} = \frac{B'C'}{BC} = \frac{VC'}{VC} = \quad \text{etc.}$$

or

$$\frac{A'B'}{AB} = \frac{B'C'}{BC} = \frac{C'D'}{CD} = \quad \text{etc.}$$

And since the angles of the polygon that is the section equal respectively, the angles of the polygon that is the base, then

$$ABCDE \sim A'B'C'D'E'$$

Q.E.D. (second part)

The student should supply reasons for the above outlined proof.

Theorem 41. The area of a section of a pyramid parallel to the base is to the area of the base as the square of its distance from the vertex is to the square of the altitude of the pyramid.

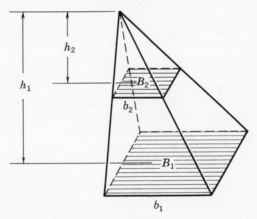

FIG. 33

Denoting: Area of the base as B_1.

Area of the section as B_2.

Height of the pyramid as h_1.

Distance of section *from vertex* as h_2.

We have, from similar triangles,

$$\frac{h_2}{h_1} = \frac{b_2}{b_1}$$

Or

$$\frac{h_2^2}{h_1^2} = \frac{b_2^2}{b_1^2}$$

But

$$\frac{B_2}{B_1} = \frac{b_2^2}{b_1^2}$$

(The areas of two similar polygons are to each other as the squares of two corresponding sides.)

$$\therefore \frac{B_2}{B_1} = \frac{h_2^2}{h_1^2}$$

Q.E.D.

PROBLEMS

1. Given a regular square pyramid with an edge of the base 12 inches and slant height 8 inches find its lateral area.

2. Given a regular square pyramid with an edge of the base 12 inches and an altitude of 8 inches find its lateral area.

3. Given a regular hexagonal pyramid with an edge of the base 4 inches and an altitude of 10 inches find its lateral area.

4. Given a regular hexagonal pyramid with an edge of the base 6 inches and a slant height of 14 inches find its lateral area.

5. If the slant height of a regular square pyramid is 8 inches and its lateral area is 96 square inches, find the length of a side of the base.

6. If a regular square pyramid with an edge of the base 8 inches and an altitude of 9 inches is cut by a plane parallel to the base and 3 inches below the vertex, what is the area of the section so formed?

7. If a regular hexagonal pyramid with an altitude of 12 inches and an edge of the base 6 inches is cut by a plane parallel to the base and 6 inches below the vertex, what is the area of the section so formed?

8. If a regular square pyramid with side of the base 6 inches and altitude 8 inches is cut by a plane parallel to the base and 2

inches above it, what is the length of a side of the section so
formed?

9. A regular triangular pyramid has an altitude of 9 inches and
a side of the base equal to 3 inches.   Find its lateral area.
(It may help to recall that the altitudes of an equilateral
triangle meet in a point two-thirds of the altitude from the
vertex.)

10. Find the total area of a regular hexagonal pyramid whose
altitude is 8 inches if a side of the base is 4 inches.

**Postulate. Triangular pyramids with equal altitudes and
equal bases have equal volumes.**

Note that this postulate requires that the bases be equal but
not necessarily congruent.   Therefore, although we postulate
that the pyramids are of equal volume, they are not
necessarily congruent.

The preceding postulate could be proved as a theorem by using
some ideas and notations for limits and sums.   The following
intuitive justification should prove reasonably satisfactory
for those students who consider the postulate an unlikely one.

Consider two triangular pyramids $ABC—V$ and $A'B'C'—V'$ as
shown in Fig. 34.   Triangles ABC and $A'B'C'$ are equal in
area (but not necessarily congruent) and both pyramids have

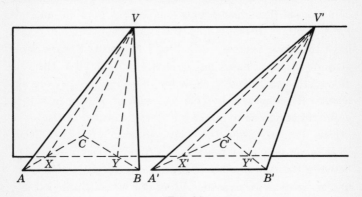

Fig. 34

the same altitude. Let the bases of both pyramids be in the same plane and then cut both pyramids into "slices" with a series of planes parallel to the bases. Using the intersections of these planes with the pyramids as bases, construct a series of triangular right prisms between the planes. These triangular prisms are shown in the cross-sectional views XYV and $X'Y'V'$ (Fig. 35). (The plane forming these sections is a plane determined by the two altitudes.)

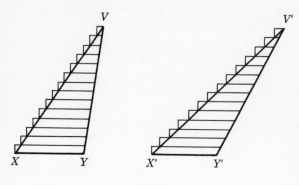

Fɪɢ. 35

For each pyramid the sum of the triangular prisms associated with it is somewhat greater than the volume of the pyramid. The pairs of triangular prisms (one for one pyramid and one for the other) between any two successive cutting planes have the same volume. (Each pair of prisms has the same altitude and their bases may be shown to be equal. Theorem 40 could be employed to show the bases *equal*—they are not necessarily congruent.) Then the sum of the set of prisms approximating one pyramid is equal to the sum of the set of prisms approximating the other pyramid. If our "slices" were taken very close together, we could make the difference between the sum of a set of prisms and the associated pyramid as small as we pleased. From this we conclude that it is reasonable to assume that the pyramids have the same volume. This theorem that we have postulated is actually a special case of Cavalieri's theorem, which states that two geometric solids included between two parallel planes are equal (have the same volume) if the sections made by planes parallel to and at the same distance from their respective plane bases are always equal. We will not need this more general form however.

Theorem 42. The volume of a triangular pyramid is equal to one-third the product of the area of its base and its altitude

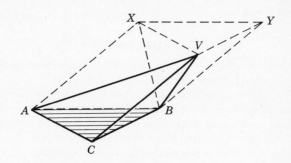

Fig. 36

Given: The triangular pyramid $V—ABC$

Construct a triangular prism with bases ABC and VXY with AX and BY lateral edges parallel to CV.

$\triangle BXY \cong \triangle BAX$. (Why?)

$\triangle VXA \cong \triangle VCA$. (Why?)

Triangular pyramids $V—BXY$ and $V—BAX$ have the common vertex V and therefore the same altitude.

$V—BXY = V—BAX$ (equal in volume but not necessarily congruent) by the immediately preceding postulate.

Similarly $B—VAC = B—VXA$.

$\therefore V—BXY = V—BAX = V—BAC$. (Why?)

Denoting the area of ABC as B and the altitude of both the triangular prism and the triangular pyramid $V—ABC$ by h, volume of $V—ABC = \dfrac{1}{3}$ volume of the triangular prism.

Volume of $V—ABC = \dfrac{1}{3}Bh$.

In formula form, the volume of any triangular pyramid is

$$V = \frac{1}{3}Bh.$$

The volume of any pyramid is equal to one-third the product of the area of its base and its altitude ($V = \frac{1}{3}Bh$). (To prove this divide the pyramid into triangular pyramids and apply Theorem 42.)

PROBLEMS

1. Find the volume of a regular square pyramid with an edge of the base 12 inches and an altitude of 8 inches.
2. Find the volume of a regular square pyramid with an edge of the base 6 inches and a slant height of 8 inches.
3. Find the volume of a regular hexagonal pyramid with an edge of the base 4 inches and an altitude of 10 inches.
4. Find the volume of a regular hexagonal pyramid with an edge of the base 6 inches and a slant height of 14 inches.
5. If the volume of a regular square pyramid is 144 cubic inches and its altitude is 12 inches find the length of a side of the base.
6. Find the slant height of the pyramid in Problem 5.
7. A regular triangular pyramid has an altitude of 9 inches and a side of the base equal to 3 inches. Find its volume.
8. A triangular pyramid has sides of the base equal to 4 inches, 5 inches, and 6 inches and an altitude of 8 inches. Find the volume of the pyramid.
9. A regular hexagonal prism and a regular hexagonal pyramid have the same altitude and volume. If a side of the base of the pyramid is 4 inches, what is a side of the base of the prism?
10. If a regular square pyramid is to have its volume doubled while the height remains constant, what change must be made in the length of a side of the base?
11. In Problem 10 what would happen to the volume if the side of the base were doubled?

12. If a pyramid has a base in the form of a trapezoid (upper base 4 inches, lower base 8 inches, altitude of the trapezoid 3 inches) and an altitude of 6 inches, what is the volume of the pyramid?

13. If the slant height of a regular square pyramid is 8 inches and the altitude is 6 inches, find the volume of the pyramid.

14. If the slant height of a regular square pyramid is 10 inches and an edge of the base is 12 inches, find the volume of the pyramid.

15. If the slant height of a regular hexagonal pyramid is 12 inches and the altitude of the pyramid is 5 inches, find the volume of the pyramid.

Frustums of Pyramids

A **frustum** of a pyramid is the geometric solid bounded by the base of a pyramid, a plane parallel to the base between the base and the vertex, and the portions of the lateral faces of the pyramid included between this plane and the base of the pyramid.   (The plural of *frustum* is *frustums*, although *frusta* is sometimes used.)

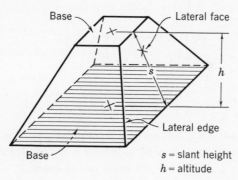

Fig. 37

Lateral faces, altitude, bases, lateral edges, and slant height are defined as implied in Fig. 37.   The smaller base is often called the upper base.

Note: If a pyramid is cut by a plane *not* parallel to the base, the two geometric solids into which the pyramid is divided are called a pyramid and a *truncated pyramid*.

Theorem 43. The lateral area of a frustum of a *regular* pyramid is equal to one-half the product of the slant height and the sum of the perimeters of the bases.

Since the lateral faces are congruent isosceles trapezoids the lateral area (L) equals nA where A is the area of one lateral face and n the number of faces.

$$L = nA$$

But

$$A = \frac{1}{2} s(b + b')$$

Where s is the slant height and b and b' are sides of the upper and lower bases.

$$\therefore \ L = n\left[\frac{1}{2} s(b + b')\right] = \frac{1}{2} s(nb + nb')$$

But nb and nb' are perimeters of the bases.
Denoting these perimeters by p and p' we have

$$L = \frac{1}{2} s(p + p')$$

Theorem 44. The volume of a frustum of a pyramid is given by $V = \frac{1}{3} h(B + B' + \sqrt{BB'})$, where h is the altitude of the frustum and B and B' are the areas of the bases.

Given: The frustum shown in Fig. 38 (cut from a pyramid of height $h + c$ to yield a frustum of height h with upper base B' and lower base B).

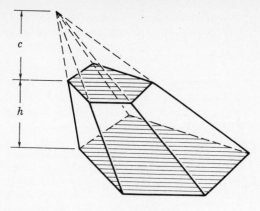

Fig. 38

Let V denote the volume of the frustum.

$$V = \frac{1}{3}(h + c)B - \frac{1}{3}cB'$$ Difference of volumes of two pyramids.

$$\frac{B}{B'} = \frac{(h + c)^2}{c^2}$$ Why?

$$c = \frac{h\sqrt{B'}}{\sqrt{B} - \sqrt{B'}}$$ Solving above for c (take square root of both sides first).

$\therefore$

$$V = \frac{1}{3}h(B + B' + \sqrt{BB'})$$ Substituting above value for c in first step. In simplification it may help to observe that

$$\frac{B - B'}{\sqrt{B} - \sqrt{B'}} = \sqrt{B} + \sqrt{B'}$$

Q.E.D.

Consider a numerical example in problem solving for the determination of slant heights or altitudes in frustums of regular pyramids.

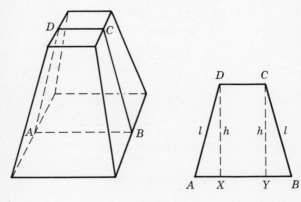

FIG. 39

Given: A regular square pyramid, side of upper base 4 inches, side of lower base 8 inches, and height 5 inches.

The section $ABCD$ ($\perp$ to the bases) is an isosceles trapezoid; $DC = 4$ inches, $AD = 8$ inches, and $h = 5$ inches.

Hence $XY = 4$ inches and $AX = YB = 2$ inches.

Then by the Pythagorean theorem $l^2 = h^2 + \overline{AX}^2$.

Hence $l = \sqrt{29}$.

A similar analysis will yield h if l and the sides of the base are the known data.

Note. For a regular hexagonal pyramid the bases of the comparable isosceles trapezoids will be distances *across the flats* of the hexagonal bases.

PROBLEMS

1. Find the volume of each of the following frustums of regular square pyramids:

	Lower Base Edge	Upper Base Edge	Height of Frustum
a.	9″	3″	4″
b.	6″	4″	9″
c.	10″	5″	7″

2. For each of the frustums in Problem 1 find the lateral area.

3. Find the volume of a frustum of a regular hexagonal pyramid if the side of the lower base is 4 inches, side of the upper base 2 inches, height of the frustum 6 inches.

4. Find the volume of a frustum of a regular square pyramid formed by cutting off a pyramid whose lower base is 9″ × 9″ and whose altitude is 1 foot by a plane 6 inches from the vertex.

5. Find the lateral area of the frustum in Problem 3.

6. Find the total area of the frustum in Problem 4.

7. What is the altitude of a frustum of a regular square pyramid whose upper base is 2″ × 2″ and whose lower base is 4″ × 4″ if it is to have the same volume as a cube 3 inches on an edge?

8. If the edge of the lower base of a frustum of a regular hexagonal pyramid is 9 inches and the upper base has half the area of the lower base, what is the volume of the frustum if its altitude is 6 inches?

9. A regular triangular pyramid 6 inches high, 4 inches on the side of the base is cut off by a plane 2 inches from the vertex. Find the volume of the frustum so formed.

10. What is the lateral area of the frustum in Problem 8?

CHAPTER 3

Cylinders

A **closed cylindrical surface** is the surface generated by a straight line moving so as to remain parallel to a given straight line and continuously intersect a given closed curve. (*Cylindric* is occasionally used for *Cylindrical*.)

The moving line in any of its positions is called an **element** of the cylindrical surface.

A **cylinder** is the geometric solid bounded by the portion of a cylindrical surface included between two parallel planes that cut all the elements, and the two parallel planes.

The finite portions of the two parallel planes cut off by the cylindrical surface are called the **bases** of the cylinder.

The portion of any element of the cylindrical surface included between the parallel planes is called an **element** of the cylinder.

If the elements are perpendicular to the bases, the cylinder is called a **right cylinder**; otherwise it is called an **oblique cylinder**.

The **lateral area** of a cylinder is the area of the portion of the cylindrical surface included between the bases.

Cylinders are classified according to the shapes of their bases; e.g., if the base is a circle, the cylinder is a **circular cylinder**.

A right circular cylinder is also called a **cylinder of revolution**. If a rectangle is rotated about one side a right circular cylinder is generated.

It can easily be shown that *the elements of a cylinder are all equal and parallel*.

Note that an element of a right cylinder is equal to the altitude of the right cylinder.

A prism is said to be inscribed in a cylinder if the bases of the prism are inscribed in the bases of the cylinder. If the lateral edges of the prism coincide with elements of the cylinder, the cylinder is said to be circumscribed about the prism.

A prism is said to be circumscribed about a cylinder if the bases of the prism are circumscribed about the bases of the cylinder. If the lateral faces of the prism are all tangent to the cylinder, the cylinder is said to be inscribed in the prism.

A **right section** of a cylinder is the section formed by a plane cutting all elements, or the elements extended, and perpendicular to them.

QUESTIONS

1. May a right cylinder be a circular cylinder?
2. May a circular cylinder be an oblique cylinder?
3. May a cylinder of revolution be an oblique cylinder?
4. Is an element of a cylinder always equal to an altitude of the cylinder?
5. May an elliptical cylinder be a right cylinder?

Postulate. The bases of a cylinder are congruent and all right sections of a cylinder are congruent.

Therefore the base of a right cylinder is congruent to a right section of the right cylinder.

Theorem 45. The lateral area of a circular cylinder is equal to the product of an element and the perimeter of a right section.

Given: A cylinder in which is inscribed a prism whose bases are regular polygons (shown as squares in Fig. 40).

Fig. 40

Denote the lateral area of this prism as S', the perimeter of its right section as p' and its lateral edge as e (which is identically an element of the cylinder).

$S' = p'e.$ Application of the usual formula for lateral area of a prism.

Now increase the number of lateral faces of the prism keeping the base regular. A convenient way to do this is to bisect each arc subtended by each side of a base and connect these points, obtaining successively octagons, 16-gons, 32-gons, etc.

S' will now approach S.   The lateral area of the cylinder.

Written $S' \rightarrow S$.   Actually we are postulating the existence of this limit and defining it to be the lateral area of the cylinder.

$p' \rightarrow p$.   Where p is the perimeter of the right section of the cylinder.

Since for each successive prism

$$S' = p'e$$

And

$$S' \to S \text{ while } p' \to p$$

We conclude

$$S = pe$$

Q.E.D.

The last step involves postulating a theorem on limits, namely:

If $x = ya$
And $x \to X$ as $y \to Y$
Then $X = Ya$

Note that for all circular cylinders we now have

$$S = pe$$

Where p is the perimeter of a right section.

In cylinders of revolution (right circular cylinders) the perimeter of the base is the perimeter of a right section.

Theorem 46. The volume of a circular cylinder is equal to the product of the area of its base and its altitude.

Given: Fig. 40 for Theorem 45.

Denoting the areas of the bases of the prisms by b', the area of the base of the cylinder by B, and the height of the cylinder (also of the prisms) by h, the volume of the prisms by V', and the volume of the cylinder by V:

$V' = b'h.$	Usual formula for prisms.
$b' \to B.$	These limits are assumed to exist and
$V' \to V.$	this is actually a definition of V.
Then $V = Bh.$	From our postulated theorem on limits.

Note that for a right cylinder h and e will be identical.

PROBLEMS

1. Find the lateral area of a right circular cylinder if the radius of the base is 4 inches and the altitude is 6 inches.
2. Find the volume of the cylinder in Problem 1.
3. If the volume of a right circular cylinder is 400π cubic inches and the altitude is 10 inches, find the radius of the base.
4. If the volume of a right circular cylinder is numerically equal (in cubic inches) to its lateral area (in square inches), what is the radius of the base?
5. If the lateral area of a cylinder of revolution is 400π square inches and the altitude of the cylinder is 20 inches, what is its volume?
6. A right circular cylinder is generated by revolving a $4'' \times 8''$ rectangle about the 8-inch side. What is the volume of the cylinder so generated?
7. What is the lateral area of the cylinder in Problem 6?
8. Find the total area of the cylinder in Problem 6.
9. A cylinder is inscribed in a 4-inch cube. What is the volume of the cylinder?
10. A cylinder is circumscribed about a 4-inch cube. What is the volume of the cylinder?
11. Two cylinders have the same altitude but the radius of the base of one is twice the radius of the base of the second. What is the ratio of the volume of the first to the second?
12. In Problem 11 what is the ratio of the lateral area of the first to the second?
13. A cylinder is inscribed in a right hexagonal prism. If a side of the base of the prism is 4 inches and the altitude of the prism is 8 inches, what is the volume of the cylinder?
14. What is the lateral area of the cylinder in Problem 13?

CHAPTER 4

Cones

A **conical surface** is the surface generated by a straight line moving so as to intersect continuously a given closed plane curve and at the same time pass through a given point not coplanar with the given curve.

The **vertex** of the conical surface is the given point (above).

The generating line in any of its positions is called an **element** of the conical surface.

The two portions of the conical surface (either side of the vertex) are called the upper and lower **nappes.** (The choice of which one is upper is arbitrary.)

A **cone** is the geometric solid bounded by one nappe of a conical surface and plane, not through the vertex, cutting all elements.

Base (B), altitude (h), and elements $(e_1, e_2,$ etc.) are defined as implied by the drawing.

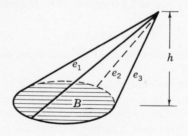

Fig. 41

Note that in general the elements of a cone are not necessarily equal.

A **circular cone** is a cone whose base is a circle.

The **axis** of a circular cone is the straight line passing through the vertex and the center of the base.

A **right circular cone** (also called a **cone of revolution**) is a circular cone whose axis is perpendicular to its base.

The **slant height** of a right circular cone is the length of one of its elements.   (Note that in a right circular cone these are all equal.)

Theorem 47. The lateral area of a cone of revolution is equal to one-half the product of the slant height (*s*) and the perimeter of the base (*p*).

$$\text{Lateral Area} = \frac{1}{2}\,ps$$

Theorem 48. The volume of a circular cone is equal to one-third the product of the area of the base (*B*) and the altitude (*h*).

$$\text{Volume} = \frac{1}{3}\,Bh$$

The proofs of the above two theorems are very similar to the analogous ones for cylinders.   It would be profitable for the student to write out at least one of the above in detail.

PROBLEMS

1. For each of the following right circular cones find the volume and the lateral area.
    a. Slant height 4 inches, radius of the base 3 inches.
    b. Slant height 7 inches, radius of the base 4 inches.
    c. Altitude 5 inches, radius of the base 6 inches.
    d. Diameter of the base 8 inches, altitude 5 inches.
    e. Slant height 12 inches, altitude 8 inches.

2. If the slant height of a cone is 10 inches and its altitude is 8 inches, find the total area of the cone (right circular cone).

3. If a right circular cone and a cylinder of revolution have congruent bases and the same altitude, what is the ratio of the volume of the cone to the volume of the cylinder?

4. If a cone is inscribed in a regular square pyramid (4 inches on a side of the base and 6 inches high), what is the volume of the cone?

5. A right circular cone is generated by revolving a right triangle whose legs are 6 inches and 8 inches about the longer leg. What is the volume of the cone so generated?

6. If the cone in Problem 5 had been generated by revolving the triangle about the shorter leg instead, what would the volume have been?

7. What is the lateral area of the cone in Problem 6?

8. If the lateral area of a cone of revolution in square inches is numerically twice its volume in cubic inches, what is the radius of the cone? The altitude of the cone is 2 inches.

Frustums of Cones

A **frustum of a cone** is the portion of a cone between the base and a section of the cone parallel to the base.

The base of the cone is called the **lower base** of the frustum while the section is called the **upper base**.

The distance between the bases of the frustum is the **altitude** of the frustum.

The **slant height** of the frustum of a right circular cone is the portion of the slant height of the cone included between the bases.

Theorem 49. The lateral area of a frustum of a right circular cone is given by

$$\text{Lateral Area} = \frac{1}{2} s(p + p'),$$

where s is the slant height of the frustum and p and p' the perimeters of the upper and lower bases.

Theorem 50. The volume of a frustum of a right circular cone is given by

$$V = \frac{1}{3} h(B + B' + \sqrt{BB'}),$$

where h is the altitude of the frustum and B and B' are the areas of the upper and lower bases.

The proofs of Theorems 49 and 50 are similar to those for cones and cylinders. (It may be noted that additional postulates regarding limits are required to take care of the sums and the radical.)

EXAMPLE

Given: A frustum of a right circular cone, of altitude 6 inches. The radius of the upper base is 8 inches and the radius of the lower base is 10 inches.

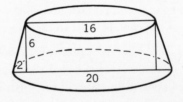

FIG. 42

To find the volume:

$$V = \frac{1}{3}(6)(\pi 8^2 + \pi 10^2 + \sqrt{\pi 8^2 \pi 10^2})$$

$$= 2(64\pi + 100\pi + 80\pi)$$

$$= 488\pi \text{ cu.in.}$$

To find the slant height for use in the lateral area formula:

$$s^2 = 6^2 + 2^2$$

$$s^2 = 40$$

$$s = \sqrt{40} = 2\sqrt{10}$$

Then to find the lateral area:

$$A = \frac{1}{2}(2\sqrt{10})(16\pi + 20\pi)$$

$$= \sqrt{10}\ (36\pi) = 36\pi\sqrt{10}\ \text{sq.in.}$$

PROBLEMS

1. For the following frustums of right circular cones find the volume and lateral area. (Heights and slant heights given are of the frustums.)
   a. Radius of the lower base 6 inches, radius of the upper base 3 inches, height 4 inches.
   b. Radius of the lower base 2 inches, radius of the upper base 1 inch, height 1 inch.
   c. Radius of the lower base 6 inches, radius of the upper base 3 inches, slant height 4 inches.
   d. Radius of the lower base 10 inches, radius of the upper base 8 inches, height 5 inches.
   e. Diameter of the lower base 6 inches, diameter of the upper base 3 inches, height 5 inches.

2. A right circular cone, radius of the base 6 inches and altitude 8 inches is cut by a plane parallel to the base and 4 inches above it. Find the volume of the frustum so formed.

3. A frustum of a regular square pyramid (edge of lower base 6 inches, edge of upper base 3 inches, height of frustum 2 inches) has a frustum of a circular cone inscribed in it. What is the volume of this frustum of a cone?

4. The radius of the upper base of a frustum of a right circular cone is 10 inches and the radius of the lower base is 30 inches. How high must the frustum be in order that its volume shall be 800 cubic inches?

5. A right circular cone 10 inches high (radius of the base 6 inches)

is cut by a plane parallel to the base and 2 inches below the
vertex.   What is the volume of the frustum so formed?

6. What is the total area of a frustum of a right circular cone,
   radius of the upper base 8 inches, area of the lower base 144π
   square inches and altitude of the frustum 6 inches?

CHAPTER 5

Spheres

A **sphere** is the locus of all points equidistant from a fixed point called the center.

A **radius** of a sphere is a straight-line segment from the center to any point of the sphere.

A **diameter** of a sphere is a straight-line segment through the center of the sphere and terminated by the surface of the sphere. A diameter is therefore twice a radius.

Equal spheres (i.e., congruent spheres) have equal radii and diameters.

A point is said to be in, on, or outside a sphere according as its distance from the center is less than, equal to, or greater than a radius.

Theorem 51. Every section of a sphere made by a plane is a circle.

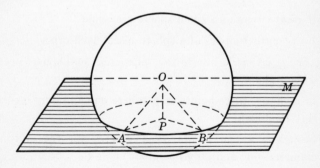

Fig. 43

65

Given: The sphere, center at O, cut by plane M

Construct OP, the $\perp$ from O to M.

Let A and B be any two points on the intersection of the sphere and the plane.

OUTLINE OF PROOF

Prove $\triangle OPA \cong \triangle OPB$ to get $PA = PB$ to conclude the intersection is a circle.

Completion of the proof is left for the student.

Suppose the plane passed through the center of the circle. The theorem still holds. How do you justify it in this case?

DEFINITIONS AND POSTULATES

*Circles of a sphere made by planes equidistant from the center are equal.[1]

A **great circle** of a sphere is a section of the sphere made by a plane through the center of the sphere.

A **small circle** of a sphere is a section of the sphere made by a plane not through the center of the sphere.

The **axis** of a circle is the diameter of the sphere perpendicular to the plane of the circle. The ends of this diameter are the **poles** of the circle.

All great circles of a given sphere are equal.

Any two great circles of a sphere bisect each other.

Every great circle bisects the sphere. A half-sphere is called a **hemisphere.**

Through any three points on a sphere one and only one circle may be drawn.

Through any two points on a sphere, not the ends of a diameter, one and only one great circle may be drawn.

[1] Starred postulates may be easily proved as exercises.

The distance between two points on the surface of a sphere is the length of the minor arc of the great circle joining them.

A quadrant is one-fourth of a great circle.

*The spherical distances of all points on a circle of a sphere from a given pole of the circle are equal.

Definitions

A plane is tangent to a sphere if the plane and the sphere have one and only one point in common.

A line is tangent to a sphere if the line and the sphere have one and only one point in common.

Two spheres are tangent to each other if they have one and only one point in common.

A sphere is inscribed in a polyhedron if every face of the polyhedron is tangent to the sphere. (The polyhedron is circumscribed about the sphere.)

A sphere is circumscribed about a polyhedron if every vertex of the polyhedron lies on the sphere. (The polyhedron is inscribed in the sphere.)

Postulates

The plane perpendicular to a radius of a sphere at its outer extremity is tangent to the sphere and conversely.

The intersection of two spheres is a circle whose plane is perpendicular to the line joining the centers of the spheres.

A sphere may be inscribed in or circumscribed about any given tetrahedron (or polyhedron of four faces).

Four noncoplanar points determine a sphere.

In a longer course these are proved as theorems.

Spherical Angles and Polygons

The angle between two intersecting curves is the smaller of the two angles formed by the tangents to the curves at the point of intersection.

A **spherical angle** is the angle between two great circles.

Consider the circle with center O as shown in Fig. 44.

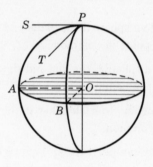

Fig. 44

The spherical angle between the great circle arcs PA and PB is defined as the angle SPT. It is evidently equal to $\angle AOB$ and measured by arc AB. (AB is on the great circle for which P is a pole.)

Vertical spherical angles, right spherical angles, adjacent spherical angles, etc., are defined similarly to the corresponding cases for plane angles.

A **spherical polygon** is a figure on a sphere, inclosed by great circle arcs.

A **spherical triangle** is a spherical polygon bounded by three great circle arcs.

Angles, sides, and vertices are defined for spherical polygons similarly to the corresponding cases for plane polygons.

A **lune** is the part of a sphere included between the halves of two great circles.

The **angle of the lune** is one of the spherical angles formed by the arcs bounding the lune.

A **spherical degree** is the area of a spherical triangle two of whose sides are quadrants and whose third side is a 1° arc.

Note that a spherical degree is a unit of *area* whose size in square units depends upon the size of the sphere. From the above definition, we easily conclude that the area of a 1° lune is two spherical degrees and that the area of any sphere is 720 spherical degrees.

Area of a sphere *(S)* (in square units)

$$S = 4\pi R^2$$

We do not derive this formula here because it can be obtained neatly by calculus later. The derivation by calculus does not depend upon any solid geometry beyond that covered to this point.

Numerical example illustrating the relationship between area in square units and area in spherical degrees:

Consider a sphere of radius 5 inches.

Area of sphere in spherical degrees = 720 spherical degrees (as for *all* spheres).

Area of sphere in square inches = $4\pi(5)^2 = 100\pi$ square inches (for this sphere).

Area of one spherical degree in square inches = $\frac{1}{720}(100\pi) = \frac{5\pi}{36}$ square inches (for this sphere).

Area of 1° lune = 2 spherical degrees (for all 1° lunes on any sphere).

Area of a 1° lune $= 2\left(\dfrac{5\pi}{36}\right) = \dfrac{5\pi}{18}$ square inches (for a 1° lune on this sphere).

What is the area of a 5° lune on this sphere in spherical degrees? In square inches?

Area of a Lune (L) (to summarize)

$$L = 2\alpha \text{ spherical degrees}$$
$$L = \frac{\alpha S}{360} \text{ square units}$$

Where α is the angle of the lune and S is the area of the sphere in square inches.

In order to obtain an important theorem regarding the angles of a spherical triangle from which we shall derive a formula for the area of a spherical triangle we now define some terms and prove a few preliminary theorems.

A **polyhedral angle** is the figure formed by a moving ray (or half-line) that continuously intersects a given plane polygon.

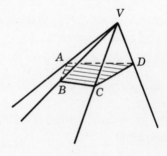

FIG. 45

Associated terminology is illustrated in Fig. 45. V is the *vertex* of the polyhedral angle. Lines through VA, VB, VC, and VD are the *edges* of the polyhedral angle. $\angle$s AVB, BVC, CVD, and DVA are *face angles* of the polyhedral angle.

Vertical polyhedral angles are two polyhedral angles in which the edges of one are extensions of the edges of the other.

Symmetric polyhedral angles are two polyhedral angles (with the same number of face angles) in which the face angles of one are equal to the face angles of the other but arranged in opposite order.

A trihedral angle is a polyhedral angle with three faces.

Trihedral angles are classified as
    Isosceles—if two face angles are equal.
    Rectangular—if one face angle is a right angle.
    Birectangular—if two face angles are right angles.
    Trirectangular—if three face angles are right angles.

The following construction may help to illustrate the concepts of vertical, symmetric, and congruent as applied to polyhedral angles.

Construct, of folded paper, two trihedral angle models with the face angles of one equal to the face angles of the other. (Do not make models isosceles.) If the pair you made are congruent (can be made to coincide) construct one symmetric to the ones you made. If the pair you made are symmetric construct one congruent to one of them. Which two, if any, can be placed in the position of vertical polyhedral angles?

Although not all symmetric trihedral angles are congruent note that *symmetric isosceles trihedral angles are congruent.*

Postulate. The sum of the face angles of a polyhedral angle is less than 360°.

(Note that at 360° the polyhedral angle "flattens out".)

From the above postulate it follows that *the sum of the sides of a convex spherical polygon is less than* 360°. (Convex is here used in essentially the same sense as when applied to plane polygons.)

One spherical triangle is the **polar triangle** of another spherical triangle if the vertices of the second are poles of the sides of the first.

Theorem 52. If the first of two spherical triangles is the polar of the second, then the second is the polar of the first.

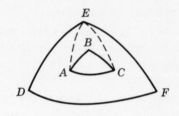

Fig. 46

Given: $\triangle DEF$ is polar of $\triangle ABC$
To prove: $\triangle ABC$ is polar of $\triangle DEF$

Draw great circle arcs EA and EC.
Arcs EA and EC are each quadrants.
$\therefore$ E is the pole of $\widehat{AC}$. (Check the definition of pole; it will take more than one step to justify this statement.)
Similarly D is the pole of $\widehat{BC}$ and F is the pole of $\widehat{AB}$.
$\therefore$ $\triangle ABC$ is polar of $\triangle DEF$.   (By definition.)

Q.E.D.

The above proof is only outlined; detailed steps and reasons should be supplied.

Theorem 53. In two polar triangles each angle of one has the same measure as the supplement of the side lying opposite it in the other.

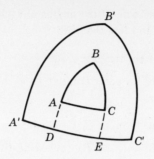

Fig. 47

Given: Polar triangles ABC and $A'B'C'$

To prove: $\angle B$ has the same measure as the supplement of $\widehat{A'C'}$

Extend $\widehat{AB}$ and $\widehat{BC}$ to meet $\widehat{A'C'}$ at D and E as in Fig. 47.

$\widehat{DE}$ has the same measure as $\angle B$.	See note after definition of spherical angles.
$\widehat{A'E} = \widehat{DC'} = 90°.$	A few steps proving this from the definition of a pole are necessary.
$\widehat{A'E} + \widehat{DC'} = 180°.$	Equals added to equals the results are equal.
$\widehat{DE} + \widehat{A'C'} = \widehat{A'E} + \widehat{DC'}.$	Why?
$\widehat{DE} + \widehat{A'C'} = 180°.$	Things equal to the same thing are equal to each other.

$\therefore \angle B$ has the same measure as the supplement $(\widehat{DE})$ of $\widehat{A'C'}$ and similarly for the other $\angle s$.

Q.E.D.

Theorem 54. The sum of the angles of a spherical triangle is greater than 180° and less than 540°.

Given: The spherical triangle ABC

Denote the sides of its polar triangle as a', b', and c' where a' is opposite A, etc.

$$\left. \begin{array}{l} \angle A + a' = 180° \\ \angle B + b' = 180° \\ \angle C + c' = 180° \end{array} \right\} \quad \text{By preceding theorem.}$$

$\angle A + \angle B + \angle C + (a' + b' + c') = 540°$.   (Why?)

$a' + b' + c' < 360°$.   (Why?)

$\therefore \ \angle A + \angle B + \angle C > 180°$.   (Why?)

Q.E.D.

$a' + b' + c' > 0$.   (Why?)

$\therefore \ \angle A + \angle B + \angle C < 540°$.   (Why?)

Q.E.D.

No figure is drawn for this theorem.   The student may find it helpful to draw one but it is not necessary.

Note that a spherical triangle may have more than one right angle or more than one obtuse angle.

A **birectangular spherical triangle** is a spherical triangle with two right angles.

A **trirectangular spherical triangle** is a spherical triangle with three right angles.

The **spherical excess of a spherical triangle** is defined as the amount by which the sum of the angles of the spherical triangle exceeds 180°.

Spherical excess could be defined for other spherical polygons but we will not do so here.

Postulate. Two spherical triangles corresponding to a pair of vertical trihedral angles are equivalent (have the same area).

Theorem 55. The area of a spherical triangle in spherical degrees is equal to its spherical excess.

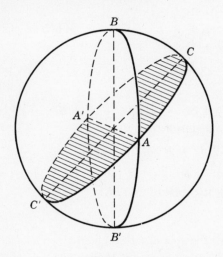

Fig. 48

Given: $\triangle ABC$

Extend sides to form great circles with diameters AA', BB', and CC'.

Reasons should be supplied for the following proof.

$\triangle$ is used throughout this proof to mean *spherical triangle*.

Lune of $\angle A = \triangle ABC + \triangle A'BC = 2A°$. $2A°$ here means $2A$ spherical degrees where A is the angle of the lune.

Lune of $\angle B = \triangle ABC + \triangle AB'C = 2B°$.

Lune of $\angle C = \triangle ABC + \triangle ABC' = 2C°$.

$\triangle ABC + \triangle A'BC + \triangle ABC + AB'C$
$\quad + \triangle ABC + \triangle ABC' = 2A° + 2B°$
$\quad + 2C°$

$2\triangle ABC = 2(A° + B° + C°) - (\triangle ABC$
$\quad + \triangle A'BC + \triangle AB'C + \triangle ABC')$

$\triangle A'BC' = \triangle AB'C$.   By preceding
                                              postulate.

$\triangle ABC + \triangle A'BC + \triangle AB'C + \triangle ABC'$
$\quad = 360°$ (a hemisphere).

$2\triangle ABC = 2(A° + B° + C°) - 360°$.

$\triangle ABC = A° + B° + C° - 180° = E$
(the spherical excess of $\triangle ABC$).

                                                   Q.E.D.

We now have the area of a triangle *in spherical degrees* is equal to E (the spherical excess of the triangle).

Since one spherical degree $= S/720$ square units where S is the area of the sphere in square units the *area of a spherical triangle in square units* is given by

$$A = \frac{ES}{720}$$

A **zone** is the portion of a sphere included between two parallel planes.

    The **bases** of the zone are the circles made by the intersections of the planes with the sphere.

    The **altitude** of the zone is the distance between the planes. If one of the planes is tangent to the sphere the resulting zone is called a **zone of one base**.

Area of a zone (Z) is given by

$$Z = 2\pi Rh$$

Where R is the radius of the sphere and h is the height of the zone.

Proof for the formula can be obtained by calculus using no solid geometry other than that presented so far and is here omitted.

Area of a zone of one base is also given by

$$Z = \pi c^2$$

Where c is the chord of the generating arc.

OUTLINE OF PROOF

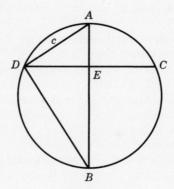

FIG. 49

Area of Zone $= 2\pi R(\overline{AE})$

$\triangle ADB \sim \triangle ADE$

$$\frac{\overline{AB}}{c} = \frac{c}{\overline{AE}}$$

$$c^2 = \overline{AE} \cdot \overline{AB} = 2R(\overline{AE})$$

$\therefore$ Area of zone $= \pi c^2$

Reasons should be supplied for the above proof.

PROBLEMS

1. Find the spherical excess of each of the following spherical triangles:
   a. Angles of the triangle: 100°, 90°, 45°.
   b. Angles of the triangle: 80°, 80°, 80°.
   c. A trirectangular triangular.
   d. Angles of the triangle: 150°, 160°, 170°.

2. Given a sphere of 6-inch radius:
   a. Find its area in spherical degrees.
   b. Find its area in square inches.

3. Given a sphere of 10-inch radius:
   a. Find the area of a 4° lune on this sphere in spherical degrees.
   b. Find the area of this same lune in square inches.

4. Find the area of an 8° lune on a sphere whose area is 400 square inches.

5. If a 2° lune on a certain sphere has an area of 18 square inches, find the area of the sphere.

6. What is the area in spherical degrees of a triangle whose angles are 60°, 80°, and 80°.

7. What is the area in square inches of a trirectangular triangle? Give answer as a function of R, the radius of the sphere.

8. What is the area in square inches of a trirectangular triangle on a sphere whose radius is 6 inches?

9. What is the area in square inches of a triangle whose angles are 100°, 75°, and 80° on a sphere whose radius is 9 inches?

10. If a triangle with the same size angles as those of the triangle in Problem 9 were drawn on a sphere whose radius was 4·5 inches, what would the area of the triangle then be?

11. What is the area in spherical degrees of the triangle in Problem 9?

12. What is the area in spherical degrees of the triangle in Problem 10?

13. What is the area in square inches of a zone whose height is 4 inches on a sphere whose diameter is 14 inches?

14. What is the area in square inches of a zone of one base on a 10-inch diameter sphere if the chord of the generating arc is 2 inches?

15. What is the area in square inches of a zone of one base on a 20-inch sphere (diameter) if the chord of the generating arc is 2 inches?

16. If a sphere is cut by two parallel planes (see Fig. 50), find the areas of each of the three resulting zones. (Diameter of the sphere is 8 inches.)

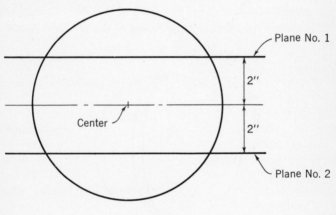

FIG. 50

17. If the diameter of a sphere is doubled, what happens to the surface area in spherical degrees? What happens to the surface area in square units?

18. If a sphere is inscribed in a cube 6 inches on an edge what is the surface area of the sphere?

19. If a sphere is circumscribed about a cube 6 inches on an edge what is the surface area of the sphere?

20. How high must a right circular cylinder (diameter of the base 4 inches) be in order to have the lateral area of the cylinder equal to the surface area of a 4-inch diameter sphere?

Spherical Volumes

Volume of a sphere of radius R is here postulated as

$$V = \frac{4}{3}\pi R^3$$

We do not derive this formula here because it can be obtained so neatly by calculus later. The derivation by calculus does not depend on any solid geometry beyond that covered to this point.

A **spherical wedge** is the geometric solid bounded by a lune and the planes passed through the sides of the lune. (Note that these planes pass through the center of the sphere. See Fig. 51.)

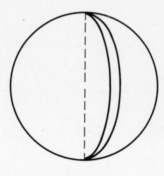

FIG. 51

If the angle of the lune is α (assumed here to be in degrees) the associated spherical wedge will have a volume of $\alpha/360$ of the sphere.

Volume of a spherical wedge (W)

$$W = \frac{\alpha V}{360}$$

Where α is the angle of the bounding lune (we call the wedge an $\alpha°$ wedge) and V is the volume of the sphere.

A **spherical sector** is the geometric solid generated by re-volving a sector of a circle about a diameter of the circle.

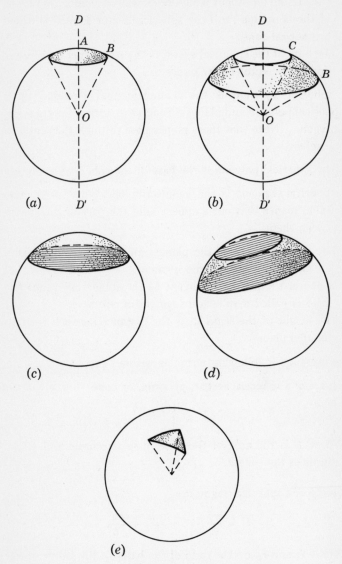

FIG. 52. Examples of Spherical Volumes

If the diameter, about which revolution is made, lies on one of the bounding radii the spherical sector formed is called a **spherical cone**.

The base of the spherical sector is the zone generated by the arc of the sector of the circle.

A **spherical pyramid** is the geometric solid bounded by a spherical polygon and planes through the sides of the spherical polygon. (Note that these planes pass through the center of the sphere.)

The spherical polygon is the **base** of the spherical pyramid.

A **spherical segment** is the geometric solid bounded by two parallel planes that cut a sphere, and the part of the sphere between them.

The finite portions of the planes intercepted by the sphere are called the **bases** of the segment.

If one of the planes is tangent to the sphere the geometric solid is called a **spherical segment of one base**.

The **height** of the segment is the distance between the two parallel planes.

We present the following formulas without proof:

Volume of a spherical sector, pyramid, or cone

$$V = \frac{1}{3} BR$$

Where B is the area of the base in square units and R the radius of the sphere.

Volume of a spherical segment

$$V = \frac{\pi h}{2} \left(r_1{}^2 + r_2{}^2 \right) + \frac{\pi h^3}{6}$$

Where r_1 and r_2 are the radii of the bases of the segment and h the altitude of the segment.

Volume of a spherical segment of one base

$$V = \frac{\pi h r^2}{2} + \frac{\pi h^3}{6}$$

Where r is the radius of the base and h the height of the segment.

PROBLEMS

1. Find the volume of a sphere whose radius is 9 inches.
2. Find the volume of a sphere whose radius is 1/2 inch.
3. Find the volume of a sphere whose diameter is 4 inches.
4. Find the volume of a sphere whose area is 400π square inches.
5. Find the volume of a sphere inscribed in a cube 6 inches on an edge.
6. Find the volume of a sphere circumscribed about a cube 8 inches on an edge.
7. If a right circular cylinder 4 inches high is to have the same volume as a sphere whose diameter is 4 inches, what must the diameter of the base of the cylinder be?
8. What is the volume of an 8° wedge cut from a sphere whose radius is 4 inches?
9. What is the volume of a spherical wedge cut from a 10-inch diameter sphere if the angle of the bounding lune is 4°?
10. What must be the angle of a spherical wedge on a 6-inch radius sphere in order that the wedge shall contain 1/8 of the volume of the sphere?
11. If a zone of one base, such that the height of the zone is 4 inches, forms the base of a spherical cone cut from an 8-inch radius sphere, what is the volume of the spherical cone?
12. A sphere is cut by a plane 4 inches from the center. If the radius of the sphere is 12 inches, what are the volumes of the two parts into which the sphere is cut?
13. Suppose that in Problem 12 a second plane, parallel to the first and 2 inches closer to the center, also cut the sphere. What would be the volumes of the three pieces into which the sphere would then be cut?
14. If the radius of a sphere is doubled, what happens to the volume?
15. Find the volume of each of the following spherical pyramids whose bases are spherical triangles:

a. ∠s of the △ 70°, 80°, 90°   Radius of the sphere is 4 inches.
b. ∠s of the △ 100°, 100°, 100°.   Radius of the sphere is 5 inches.
c. ∠s of the △ 90°, 90°, 45°.   Radius of the sphere is 6 inches.

16. A solid physical sphere 10 inches in diameter has a hole (of circular cross-section) bored through it. If the hole is 6 inches in diameter and centered (center of the hole through the center of the sphere), what is the volume of the remaining portion of the sphere?

17. Suppose that a 12-gauge shotgun is defined as a shotgun of such a size bore that 12 spherical lead balls, each of a size that will just fit the bore at the breech, will weigh one pound. If lead weighs 687.0 lb/cu ft., what is the diameter of the bore of a 12-gauge shotgun at the breech?

18. Assume the earth to be a perfect sphere and a metal band to be tightly banded about it at the equator. If this band is then cut and a 1-foot splice inserted and the band adjusted so that the clearance is the same at all points, how far off the surface of the earth will the band be? Work this same problem for a sphere of 10-inch diameter instead of the earth. What is the radius of a circle whose circumference is 1 foot? What general conclusions, if any, can be made from the answers to this problem?

CHAPTER 6

Measurement Formulas from Plane Geometry

Pythagorean Theorem. In any right triangle the square of the hypotenuse is equal to the sum of the squares of the other two sides.

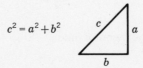

$$c^2 = a^2 + b^2$$

Fig. 53

Area of any parallelogram

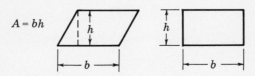

$$A = bh$$

Fig. 54

Area of any triangle

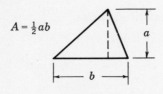

$$A = \tfrac{1}{2}ab$$

Fig. 55

Area of any triangle (given the three sides):
Heron's Formula

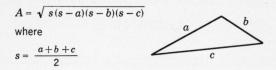

$$A = \sqrt{s(s-a)(s-b)(s-c)}$$
where
$$s = \frac{a+b+c}{2}$$

Fig. 56

Area of an equilateral triangle of side s
$$A = \frac{s^2\sqrt{3}}{4}$$

Area of a regular hexagon of side s
$$A = \frac{3s^2\sqrt{3}}{2}$$

Altitude of an equilateral triangle of side s
$$a = \frac{s\sqrt{3}}{2}$$

Area of a circle of radius r
$$A = \pi r^2$$

Circumference of a circle of radius r
$$C = 2\pi r$$

For radii of circumscribed circles

About a hexagon of side s $r = s$

About a square $r = \frac{1}{2}$ of the diagonal

About an equilateral triangle $r = \frac{2}{3}$ of the altitude

For radii of inscribed circles

In a hexagon of side s $\qquad r = \dfrac{s\sqrt{3}}{2}$

In a square $\qquad r = \dfrac{1}{2}$ of the side

In an equilateral triangle $\qquad r = \dfrac{1}{3}$ of the altitude

CHAPTER 7

Measurement Formulas from Solid Geometry

Volumes

Any prism or cylinder, where B is area of the base and h is altitude of the prism or cylinder

$$V = Bh$$

Any pyramid or cone where B is area of the base and h is altitude of the pyramid or cone

$$V = \frac{1}{3}Bh$$

A frustum of any pyramid or cone where B is the area of one base, B' the area of the other base, and h the altitude of the frustum

$$V = \frac{1}{3}h[B + B' + \sqrt{BB'}]$$

Any sphere of radius R

$$V = \frac{4}{3}\pi R^3$$

Any spherical cone, spherical pyramid, or spherical sector from a sphere of radius R, where B is the area of the base of the cone, pyramid or sector

$$V = \frac{1}{3}BR$$

Any spherical segment of two bases where r_1 is the radius of one base and r_2 the radius of the other and h is the height of the segment

$$V = \frac{\pi h}{2}(r_1{}^2 + r_2{}^2) + \frac{\pi h^3}{6}$$

For a spherical segment of one base this reduces to

$$V = \frac{\pi h r^2}{2} + \frac{\pi h^3}{6}$$

A spherical wedge cut from a sphere of volume V, where the angle of the wedge is α degrees

$$W = \frac{\alpha V}{360}$$

Surface Areas

The lateral area of any prism or cone where p is the perimeter of a right section and e is the length of a lateral edge (or element):

$$L = pe$$

The lateral area of a regular pyramid or right circular cone where p is the perimeter of the base and s is the slant height:

$$L = \frac{1}{2} ps$$

The lateral area of a frustum of a regular pyramid or right circular cone where p is the perimeter of one base, p' the perimeter of the other base, and s the slant height of the frustum

$$L = \frac{1}{2} s(p + p')$$

The surface area of any sphere of radius R

$S = 720$ spherical degrees $S = 4\pi R^2$ square units

The area of a spherical triangle of spherical excess E on a sphere of radius R

$A = E$ spherical degrees $A = \dfrac{ES}{720}$ square units

The area of any zone of height h on a sphere of radius R

$$Z = 2\pi R h$$

The area of a zone of one base given the length of the chord of the generating arc, c

$$Z = \pi c^2$$

The area of a lune on a sphere whose surface area is S and the angle of the lune is α

$$\text{L} = 2\alpha \text{ spherical degrees} \qquad L = \frac{2\alpha S}{720} \text{ square units}$$

Two theorems relative to solid geometry measurements follow

If two straight lines are cut by three or more parallel planes, their corresponding segments are proportional.

The area of a section of a pyramid (or cone) parallel to the base is to the area of the base as the square of its distance from the vertex is to the square of the altitude of the pyramid or cone.

Where the base is B_1 and the section B_2, the height of the pyramid or cone h_1, and the distance of the section from the vertex h_2

$$\frac{B_2}{B_1} = \frac{h_2^2}{h_1^2}$$

CHAPTER 8

Simplification of Radicals

For all positive real numbers, a and b, the following relations hold:

$$\sqrt[n]{ab} = \sqrt[n]{a}\,\sqrt[n]{b} \qquad \sqrt[n]{\frac{a}{b}} = \frac{\sqrt[n]{a}}{\sqrt[n]{b}}$$

These can be useful in simplifying answers to some of the problems of solid geometry. Although the relationships are stated for nth roots, it is with square roots and cube roots that we will be primarily concerned. Some examples follow:

$$\sqrt{98} = \sqrt{49(2)} = \sqrt{49}\,\sqrt{2} = 7\sqrt{2}$$

$$\sqrt{\frac{3}{4}} = \frac{\sqrt{3}}{\sqrt{4}} = \frac{\sqrt{3}}{2}$$

$$\sqrt[3]{16} = \sqrt[3]{8(2)} = \sqrt[3]{8}\sqrt[3]{2} = 2\sqrt[3]{2}$$

$$\sqrt{\pi 9^2 \pi 6^2} = \sqrt{\pi^2}\sqrt{9^2}\sqrt{6^2} = \pi(9)(6) = 54\pi$$

The following examples of an operation known as *rationalizing the denominator* illustrate another procedure useful in simplifying answers:

$$\frac{2}{\sqrt{3}} = \frac{2\sqrt{3}}{\sqrt{3}\sqrt{3}} = \frac{2\sqrt{3}}{3}$$

Note that what we have done is to multiply numerator and denominator of the original fraction by $\sqrt{3}$. Another example follows:

$$\frac{1}{\sqrt{2}} = \frac{\sqrt{2}}{\sqrt{2}\sqrt{2}} = \frac{\sqrt{2}}{2}$$

CHAPTER 9

Dihedral Angles

Any straight line in a plane divides the plane into two parts called **half-planes**. The straight line is called the edge of either half-plane.

A **dihedral angle** is the figure formed by two half-planes having a common edge.

A **plane angle of a dihedral angle** is the angle formed by two lines, one in each half-plane (or face) of a dihedral angle, and perpendicular to the common edge at the same point. All such plane angles of a given dihedral angle will be equal. A dihedral angle is measured by its plane angle. That is, a 30-degree dihedral angle is one whose plane angles are 30 degrees.

It is now possible to define planes perpendicular to each other: Two planes are said to be perpendicular to each other if they form 90 degree dihedral angles.

The following three theorems concerning perpendicular planes are often proved in a longer course:

If two planes are perpendicular to each other, any line in one of them perpendicular to their intersection is perpendicular to the other plane.

If a line is perpendicular to a plane, every plane passed through the line is perpendicular to the given plane.

If each of two intersecting planes is perpendicular to a third plane, their intersection is also perpendicular to the third plane.

CHAPTER 10

Locus

In plane geometry we observed that the locus of points equidistant from two given points is a straight line perpendicular to the line segment joining the points at the midpoint of the line segment. In solid geometry this locus will be a plane perpendicular to the line segment at its midpoint.

In plane geometry the locus of points a distance D from a given straight line is two parallel lines, each a distance D from the given straight line. In solid geometry this locus will be a cylindrical surface.

PROBLEMS

The following loci problems are intended for discussion on an intuitive basis:

1. What is the locus of points equidistant from two parallel lines?
2. What is the locus of points a distance D from a given point?
3. What is the locus of points a distance D from a given point and also a distance A from another given point? Depending upon how large D is compared to A, there are different possibilities. Each should be discussed.
4. What is the locus of points a distance D from a given plane?
5. What is the locus of points a distance D from a given plane and also a distance A from a given point? Discuss the different possibilities.
6. What is the locus of points equidistant from two parallel planes?
7. What is the locus of points equidistant from two intersecting planes?
8. What is the locus of points equidistant from two given points

and also a distance D from a given plane? Discuss the different possibilities. May this locus consist of no points?

9. What is the locus of points equidistant from the eight vertices of a cube?

10. What is the locus of points equidistant from the vertices of a given triangle? In plane geometry this is one point, the center of the circumscribed circle. We wish to consider the case for solid geometry now.

11. What is the locus of points in a given plane and also equidistant from two given points not in the given plane? Is it possible for this locus to be null (consist of no points)?

12. What is the locus of points equidistant from two intersecting lines?

13. What is the locus of points equidistant from two intersecting lines and also a distance D from the plane of the intersecting lines?

14. What is the locus of points equidistant from two intersecting lines and also a distance D from their point of intersection?

15. What is the locus of points equidistant from the vertices of a regular hexagon?

16. Consider three mutually perpendicular planes (similar to two intersecting walls and the floor of a room). Call these planes A, B, and C. What is the locus of points equidistant from A and B and a distance D from C?

17. For the planes in Problem 16 what is the locus of points equidistant from all three planes?

18. What is the locus of points lying in a given line and also equidistant from two parallel planes? There are three possibilities.

CHAPTER II

Regular Polyhedrons

A **regular polyhedron** is defined to be a polyhedron all of whose faces are congruent regular polygons and whose polyhedral angles at the vertices are congruent. Only five regular polyhedrons exist. These are sometimes called the five Platonic solids. We conclude that there cannot be more than five, as follows:

Three or more faces must meet at each vertex.

Consider the possibility of constructing regular polyhedrons whose faces are all equilateral triangles. Not more than five equilateral triangles could meet at a vertex for with six or more the sum of the face angles at the vertex would equal or exceed 360 degrees. Therefore we can consider only three possible polyhedrons constructed with faces as congruent equilateral triangles, namely, those in which 3, 4, or 5 equilateral triangles meet at each vertex.

Now consider the possibility of constructing regular polyhedrons whose faces are all squares. By a similar reasoning to that above we conclude that there is only one possibility here, namely, that in which three squares meet at each vertex. Similarly for faces of regular pentagons (since an interior angle of a regular pentagon is 108 degrees) we conclude that there is only one such possible, namely, that in which three pentagons meet at each vertex.

The above discussion leads us to conclude that not more than five regular polyhedrons are possible. We have *not* shown that there are five, or even that there are any, but only that there cannot be more than five. Actually all five of these do exist.

If three equilateral triangles meet at each vertex, we have a special case of a regular triangular pyramid called a tetrahedron. (Note that not all regular triangular pyramids are tetrahedrons.)

If four equilateral triangles meet at each vertex, we have a solid called an octahedron (it has eight faces).

If five equilateral triangles meet at each vertex, we have a solid called an icosahedron (it has twenty faces).

If three squares meet at each vertex, we have a solid called a hexahedron. There is a more common name for this one. What is it?

If three pentagons meet at each vertex, we have a solid called a dodecahedron (it has twelve faces).

Each of these regular polyhedrons may be constructed of paper by folding a one piece pattern. The student should find it fairly simple to lay out patterns for the tetrahedron and the hexahedron. Patterns for the octahedron and the dodecahedron should prove only a little more difficult (the number of faces has been given above, and this may prove helpful). The pattern for the icosahedron may prove rather difficult to discover, although a fairly simple layout is possible (it is somewhat awkward to fold). The student may find it interesting to try to construct these regular polyhedrons from his own paper patterns. These patterns may be found in a number of books, but are not included here.

Note: It is possible to have polyhedrons all of whose faces are regular polygons *not* congruent to each other. For example, one could cut off the corners of a cube to obtain a solid whose faces were regular hexagons and equilateral triangles and therefore the faces would not *all* be congruent. Such solids are not regular polyhedrons, by definition.

Suppose that on each face of a cube of side s a regular square pyramid is constructed so that the lateral faces are equilateral triangles. The resulting solid will have sixteen faces which will all be congruent equilateral triangles. This solid is not included in the five regular polyhedrons. Why not? Are there other polyhedrons of this sort?